3 1513 40025234 7

KT-144-481

HARRY POTTER

AND THE
CURSED CHILD

PARTS ONE AND TWO

BASED ON AN ORIGINAL NEW STORY BY

J.K. ROWLING

JOHN TIFFANY & JACK THORNE

A NEW PLAY BY JACK THORNE

FIRST PRODUCED BY
SONIA FRIEDMAN PRODUCTIONS, COLIN CALLENDER
& HARRY POTTER THEATRICAL PRODUCTIONS

THE OFFICIAL SCRIPT OF THE
ORIGINAL WEST END PRODUCTION

SPECIAL REHEARSAL EDITION

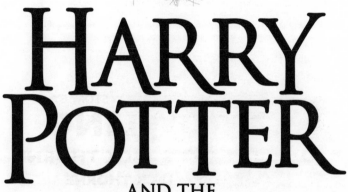

HARRY POTTER

AND THE
CURSED CHILD

PARTS ONE AND TWO

Little, Brown

LITTLE, BROWN

First published in print in Great Britain in 2016 by Little, Brown

1 3 5 7 9 10 8 6 4 2

Text © Harry Potter Theatrical Productions Limited 2016

Harry Potter Publishing and Theatrical rights © J.K. Rowling

Artwork and logo are trademarks of and © Harry Potter Theatrical Productions Limited

Harry Potter characters, names and related indicia are trademarks of
and © Warner Bros. Ent. All rights reserved.

J.K. ROWLING'S WIZARDING WORLD is a trademark of J.K. Rowling
and Warner Bros. Entertainment Inc.

*All characters and events in this publication, other than those
clearly in the public domain, are fictitious and any resemblance
to real persons, living or dead, is purely coincidental.*

All rights reserved.
No part of this publication may be reproduced, stored in a
retrieval system, or transmitted, in any form, or by any means, without
the prior permission in writing of the publisher, nor be otherwise circulated
in any form of binding or cover other than that in which it is published
and without a similar condition including this condition being
imposed on the subsequent purchaser.

A CIP catalogue record for this book is available from the British Library.

ISBN 978-0-7515-6535-5

CLACKMANNANSHIRE COUNCIL	
31513400252347	
Bertrams	29/07/2016
ROW	£20.00
ADU	AF

WITHDRAWN

An Hachette UK Company
www.hachette.co.uk

www.littlebrown.co.uk

CONTENTS

Harry Potter and the Cursed Child Parts One and Two may not be performed in whole or in part and no use may be made of it whatsoever except under express licence from the rights holders of the work, J.K. Rowling and Harry Potter Theatrical Productions Limited. Please email enquiries@hptheatricalproductions.com with any enquiries.

J.K. ROWLING

To Jack Thorne
who entered my world
and did beautiful things there.

JOHN TIFFANY

For Joe, Louis, Max, Sonny and Merle . . . wizards all . . .

JACK THORNE

To Elliott Thorne, born 7 April 2016.
As we rehearsed, he gurgled.

PART ONE

PART ONE
ACT ONE

ACT ONE SCENE ONE

KING'S CROSS

A busy and crowded station, full of people trying to go somewhere. Amongst the hustle and bustle, two large cages rattle on top of two laden trolleys. They're being pushed by two boys, JAMES POTTER *and* ALBUS POTTER. *Their mother,* GINNY, *follows after. A thirty-seven-year-old man,* HARRY, *has his daughter* LILY *on his shoulders.*

ALBUS
    Dad. He keeps saying it.

HARRY
    James, give it a rest.

JAMES
    I only said he might be in Slytherin. And he might, so . . .
    (off his dad's glare) fine.

ALBUS *(looking up at his mum)*
    You'll write to me, won't you?

GINNY
    Every day if you want us to.

ALBUS
    No. Not every day. James says most people only get letters
    from home about once a month. I don't want to . . .

HARRY

We wrote to your brother three times a week last year.

ALBUS

What? James!

ALBUS looks accusingly at JAMES.

GINNY

Yes. You may not want to believe everything he tells you about Hogwarts. He likes a laugh, your brother.

JAMES (*with a grin*)

Can we go now please?

ALBUS looks at his dad, and then his mum.

GINNY

All you have to do is walk straight at the wall between platforms nine and ten.

LILY

I'm so excited.

HARRY

Don't stop and don't be scared you'll crash into it, that's very important. Best to do it at a run if you're nervous.

ALBUS

I'm ready.

HARRY and LILY put their hands on ALBUS's trolley – GINNY joins JAMES's trolley – and together, the family run hard into the barrier.

ACT ONE SCENE TWO

PLATFORM NINE AND THREE-QUARTERS

Which is covered in thick white steam pouring from the HOGWARTS EXPRESS.

And which is also busy – but instead of people in sharp suits going about their day, it's now wizards and witches in robes mostly trying to work out how to say goodbye to their beloved progeny.

ALBUS
This is it.

LILY
Wow!

ALBUS
Platform nine and three-quarters.

LILY
Where are they? Are they here? Maybe they didn't come?

> HARRY *points out* RON, HERMIONE *and their daughter* ROSE. LILY *runs hard up to them.*

Uncle Ron. Uncle Ron!!!

> RON *turns towards them as* LILY *goes barrelling up to him. He picks her up into his arms.*

RON

If it isn't my favourite Potter.

LILY

Have you got my trick?

RON

Are you aware of the Weasleys' Wizard Wheezes certified nose-stealing breath?

ROSE

Mum! Dad's doing that lame thing again.

HERMIONE

You say lame, he says glorious, I say ... somewhere in between.

RON

Hang on. Let me just munch this ... air. And now it's just a simple matter of ... excuse me if I smell slightly of garlic ...

He breathes on her face. LILY *giggles.*

LILY

You smell of porridge.

RON

Bing. Bang. Boing. Young lady, get ready to not being able to smell at all ...

He lifts her nose off.

LILY

Where's my nose?

RON

Tada!

His hand is empty. It's a lame trick. Everyone enjoys its lameness.

LILY

You are silly.

ALBUS

Everyone's staring at us again.

RON

Because of me! I'm extremely famous. My nose experiments are legendary!

HERMIONE

They're certainly something.

HARRY

Parked all right then?

RON

I did. Hermione didn't believe I could pass a Muggle driving test, did you? She thought I'd have to Confund the examiner.

HERMIONE

I thought nothing of the kind, I have complete faith in you.

ROSE

And I have complete faith he did Confund the examiner.

RON

Oi!

ALBUS

Dad ...

ALBUS *pulls on* HARRY's *robes.* HARRY *looks down.*

Do you think – what if I am – what if I'm put in Slytherin ...

HARRY

And what would be wrong with that?

ALBUS

Slytherin is the house of the snake, of Dark Magic ... it's not a house of brave wizards.

HARRY

Albus Severus, you were named after two headmasters of Hogwarts. One of them was a Slytherin and he was probably the bravest man I ever knew.

9

ALBUS

But just say . . .

HARRY

If it matters to you, *you*, the Sorting Hat will take your feelings into account.

ALBUS

Really?

HARRY

It did for me.

This is something he's never said before, it resonates around his head a moment.

Hogwarts will be the making of you, Albus. I promise you, there is nothing to be frightened of there.

JAMES

Apart from the Thestrals. Watch out for the Thestrals.

ALBUS

I thought they were invisible!

HARRY

Listen to your professors, *don't* listen to James, and remember to enjoy yourself. Now, if you don't want this train to leave without you, you should leap on . . .

LILY

I'm going to chase the train out.

GINNY

Lily, come straight back.

HERMIONE

Rose. Remember to send Neville our love.

ROSE

Mum, I can't send a professor love!

ROSE *exits for the train. And then* ALBUS *turns and hugs* GINNY *and* HARRY *one last time before following after her.*

ALBUS

Okay, then. Bye.

He climbs on board. HERMIONE, GINNY, RON *and* HARRY *stand watching the train – as whistles blow up and down the platform.*

GINNY

They're going to be okay, right?

HERMIONE

Hogwarts is a big place.

RON

Big. Wonderful. Full of food. I'd give anything to be going back.

HARRY

Strange, Al being worried he'll be sorted into Slytherin.

HERMIONE

That's nothing, Rose is worried whether she'll break the Quidditch scoring record in her first or second year. And how early she can take her O.W.Ls.

RON

I have no idea where she gets her ambition from.

GINNY

And how would you feel Harry, if Al – if he is?

RON

You know Gin, we always thought there was a chance you could be sorted into Slytherin.

GINNY

What?

RON

Honestly, Fred and George ran a book.

HERMIONE

Can we go? People are looking, you know.

GINNY

People always look when you three are together. And apart. People always look at you.

The four exit. GINNY *stops* HARRY.

Harry . . . he'll be all right, won't he?

HARRY

Of course he will.

ACT ONE   SCENE THREE

THE HOGWARTS EXPRESS

ALBUS *and* ROSE *walk along the carriage of the train.*
The TROLLEY WITCH *approaches, pushing her trolley.*

TROLLEY WITCH
> Anything from the trolley, dears? Pumpkin Pasty?
> Chocolate Frog? Cauldron Cake?

ROSE *(spotting* ALBUS*'s loving look at the Chocolate Frogs)*
> Al. We need to concentrate.

ALBUS
> Concentrate on what?

ROSE
> On who we choose to be friends with. My mum and dad
> met your dad on their first Hogwarts Express you know ...

ALBUS
> So we need to choose now who to be friends with for life?
> That's quite scary.

ROSE
> On the contrary, it's exciting. I'm a Granger-Weasley, you're
> a Potter – everyone will want to be friends with us, we've
> got the pick of anyone we want.

ALBUS
So how do we decide – which compartment to go in . . .

ROSE
We rate them all and then we make a decision.

> ALBUS *opens a compartment door – to look in on a*
> *lonely blond kid –* SCORPIUS *– in an otherwise empty*
> *compartment.* ALBUS *smiles.* SCORPIUS *smiles back.*

ALBUS
Hi. Is this compartment . . .

SCORPIUS
It's free. It's just me.

ALBUS
Great. So we might just – come in – for a bit – if that's
okay?

SCORPIUS
That's okay. Hi.

ALBUS
Albus. Al. I'm – my name is Albus . . .

SCORPIUS
Hi Scorpius. I mean, I'm Scorpius. You're Albus. I'm
Scorpius. And you must be . . .

> ROSE's *face is growing colder by the minute.*

ROSE
Rose.

SCORPIUS
Hi Rose. Would you like some of my Fizzing Whizzbees?

ROSE
I've just had breakfast, thanks.

SCORPIUS
I've also got some Shock-o-Choc, Pepper Imps and some
Jelly Slugs. Mum's idea – she says (*sings*), 'Sweets they always

help you make friends' *(he realises that singing was a mistake)*. Stupid idea probably.

ALBUS

I'll have some ... Mum doesn't let me have sweets. Which one would you start with?

ROSE *hits* ALBUS, *out of sight of* SCORPIUS.

SCORPIUS

Easy. I've always regarded the Pepper Imp as the king of the confectionery bag. They're peppermint sweets that make you smoke at the ears.

ALBUS

Brilliant, then that's what I'll— (ROSE *hits him again.)* Rose, will you please stop hitting me?

ROSE

I'm not hitting you.

ALBUS

You are hitting me, and it hurts.

SCORPIUS's *face falls.*

SCORPIUS

She's hitting you because of me.

ALBUS

What?

SCORPIUS

Listen, I know who you are, so it's probably only fair you know who I am.

ALBUS

What do you mean you know who I am?

SCORPIUS

You're Albus Potter. She's Rose Granger-Weasley. And I am Scorpius Malfoy. My parents are Astoria and Draco Malfoy. Our parents – they didn't get on.

ROSE

That's putting it mildly. Your mum and dad are Death Eaters!

SCORPIUS (*affronted*)

Dad was – but Mum wasn't.

ROSE *looks away, and* SCORPIUS *knows why she does.*

I know what the rumour is, and it's a lie.

ALBUS *looks from an uncomfortable* ROSE *to a desperate* SCORPIUS.

ALBUS

What – is the rumour?

SCORPIUS

The *rumour* is that my parents couldn't have children. That my father and my grandfather were so desperate for a powerful heir, to prevent the end of the Malfoy line, that they ... that they used a Time-Turner to send my mother back—

ALBUS

To send her back where?

ROSE

The rumour is that he's Voldemort's son, Albus.

A *horrible, uncomfortable silence.*

It's probably rubbish. I mean ... look, you've got a nose.

The tension is slightly broken, SCORPIUS *laughs, pathetically grateful.*

SCORPIUS

And it's just like my father's! I got his nose, his hair and his name. Not that that's a great thing either. I mean – father-son issues, I have them. But, on the whole, I'd rather be a Malfoy than, you know, the son of the Dark Lord.

SCORPIUS *and* ALBUS *look at each other and something
passes between them.*

ROSE

Yes, well, we probably should sit somewhere else. Come on,
Albus.

ALBUS *is thinking deeply.*

ALBUS

No (*off* ROSE's *look*), I'm okay. You go on . . .

ROSE

Albus. I won't wait.

ALBUS

And I wouldn't expect you to. But I'm staying here.

ROSE *looks at him a second and then leaves the
compartment.*

ROSE

Fine!

SCORPIUS *and* ALBUS *are left – looking at each
other – unsure.*

SCORPIUS

Thank you.

ALBUS

No. No. I didn't stay – for you – I stayed for your sweets.

SCORPIUS

She's quite fierce.

ALBUS

Yes. Sorry.

SCORPIUS

No. I like it. Do you prefer Albus or Al?

SCORPIUS *grins and pops two sweets in his mouth.*

ALBUS *(thinks)*
Albus.

SCORPIUS *(as smoke comes out of his ears)*
THANK YOU FOR STAYING FOR MY SWEETS,
ALBUS!

ALBUS *(laughing)*
Wow.

ACT ONE SCENE FOUR

TRANSITION SCENE

And now we enter a never-world of time change. And this scene is all about magic.

The changes are rapid as we leap between worlds. There are no individual scenes, but fragments, shards that show the constant progression of time.

Initially we're inside Hogwarts, in the Great Hall, and everyone is dancing around ALBUS.

POLLY CHAPMAN
Albus Potter.

KARL JENKINS
A Potter. In our year.

YANN FREDERICKS
He's got his hair. He's got hair just like him.

ROSE
And he's my cousin. (*As they turn.*) Rose Granger-Weasley. Nice to meet you.

> *The* SORTING HAT *walks through the students who spring into their houses.*
>
> *It becomes quickly apparent he's approaching* ROSE, *who is tense as she awaits her fate.*

SORTING HAT
> I've done this job for centuries
> On every student's head I've sat
> Of thoughts I take inventories
> For I'm the famous Sorting Hat.
>
> I've sorted high, I've sorted low,
> I've done the job through thick and thin
> So put me on and you will know
> Which house you should be in ...
> Rose Granger-Weasley.

> *He puts his hat on* ROSE's *head.*

GRYFFINDOR!

> *There's cheering from the Gryffindors as* ROSE *joins them.*

ROSE
> Thank Dumbledore.

> SCORPIUS *runs to take* ROSE's *place under the* SORTING
> HAT's *glare.*

SORTING HAT
> Scorpius Malfoy.

> *He puts his hat on* SCORPIUS's *head.*

SLYTHERIN!

> SCORPIUS *was expecting this, he nods and half smiles.*
> *There's cheering from the Slytherins as he joins them.*

POLLY CHAPMAN
> Well, that makes sense.

> ALBUS *walks swiftly to the front of the stage.*

SORTING HAT
> Albus Potter.

He puts his hat on ALBUS'*s head – and this time he seems to take longer – almost like he too is confused.*

SLYTHERIN!

There's a silence.

A perfect, profound silence.

One that sits low, twists a bit and has damage within it.

POLLY CHAPMAN
Slytherin?

CRAIG BOWKER JR
Whoah! A Potter? In Slytherin.

ALBUS *looks out, unsure.* SCORPIUS *smiles, delighted, as he shouts across to him.*

SCORPIUS
You can stand next to me!

ALBUS *(thoroughly discombobulated)*
Right. Yes.

YANN FREDERICKS
I suppose his hair isn't that similar.

ROSE
Albus? But this is wrong, Albus. This is not how it's supposed to be.

And suddenly a flying lesson is happening with MADAM HOOCH.

MADAM HOOCH
Well, what are you all waiting for? Everyone stand by a broomstick. Come on, hurry up.

The kids all hurry into position beside their brooms.

Stick out your hands out over your broom, and say, 'Up!'

EVERYONE
UP!

ROSE's and YANN's brooms sail into their hands.

ROSE *and* YANN
Yes!

MADAM HOOCH
Come on now, I've no time for shirkers. Say 'UP'. 'UP' like you mean it.

EVERYONE *(bar* ROSE *and* YANN*)*
UP!

Brooms sail up, including SCORPIUS's. Only ALBUS is left with his broom on the floor.

EVERYONE *(bar* ROSE, YANN *and* ALBUS*)*
YES!

ALBUS
Up. UP. UP.

His broom doesn't move. Not even a millimetre. He stares at it with disbelieving desperation. There's giggling from the rest of the class.

POLLY CHAPMAN
Oh Merlin's beard, how humiliating! He really isn't like his father at all is he?

KARL JENKINS
Albus Potter, the Slytherin Squib.

MADAM HOOCH
Okay. Children. Time to fly.

And suddenly HARRY appears from nowhere beside ALBUS as steam expands all over the stage. We're back on platform nine and three-quarters and time has ticked on mercilessly. ALBUS is now a year older (as is HARRY, but less noticeably).

ALBUS

I'm just asking you Dad if you'll – if you'll just stand a little away from me.

HARRY *(amused)*

Second-years don't like to be seen with their dads is that it?

An OVER-ATTENTIVE WIZARD *begins to circle them.*

ALBUS

No. It's just – you're *you* and – and I'm me and—

HARRY

It's just people looking okay? People look. And they're looking at me, not you.

The OVER-ATTENTIVE WIZARD *proffers something for* HARRY *to sign – he signs it.*

ALBUS

At Harry Potter and his disappointing son.

HARRY

What does that mean?

ALBUS

At Harry Potter and his Slytherin son.

JAMES *rushes past them carrying his bag.*

JAMES

Slythering Slytherin, stop with your dithering, time to get on to the train.

HARRY

Unnecessary, James.

JAMES *(long gone)*

See you at Christmas, Dad.

HARRY *looks at* ALBUS, *concerned.*

HARRY

Al—

ALBUS

My name is Albus, not Al.

HARRY

Are the other kids being unkind? Is that it? Maybe if you tried making a few more friends – without Hermione and Ron I wouldn't have survived Hogwarts, I wouldn't have survived at all.

ALBUS

But I don't need a Ron and Hermione – I've – I've got a friend, Scorpius, and I know you don't like him but he's all I need.

HARRY

Look, as long as you're happy, that's all that matters to me.

ALBUS

You didn't need to bring me to the station, Dad.

ALBUS *picks up his case and makes hard away.*

HARRY

But I *wanted* to be here . . .

But ALBUS *is gone.* DRACO MALFOY, *his robes perfect, his blond ponytail precisely placed, emerges from within the crowds to be beside* HARRY.

DRACO

I need a favour.

HARRY

Draco.

DRACO

These rumours – about my son's parentage – they don't seem to be going away. The other Hogwarts students tease Scorpius about it relentlessly – if the Ministry could release a statement reaffirming that all Time-Turners were destroyed in the Battle of the Department of Mysteries . . .

HARRY

Draco, just let it blow over – they'll soon move on.

DRACO

My son is suffering and – Astoria hasn't been well recently – so he needs all the support he can get.

HARRY

If you answer the gossip, you feed the gossip. There've been rumours Voldemort had a child for years, Scorpius is not the first to be accused. The Ministry, for your sake as well as ours, needs to steer well clear.

DRACO *frowns, annoyed, as the stage clears and* ROSE *and* ALBUS *stand ready with their cases.*

ALBUS

As soon as the train leaves you don't have to talk to me.

ROSE

I know. We just need to keep the pretence up in front of the grown-ups.

SCORPIUS *runs on – with big hopes and an even bigger case.*

SCORPIUS *(hopeful)*
Hi Rose.

ROSE *(definitive)*
Bye Albus.

SCORPIUS *(still hopeful)*
She's melting.

And suddenly we're in the Great Hall and PROFESSOR McGONAGALL *is standing at the front, with a big smile on her face.*

PROFESSOR McGONAGALL

And I'm pleased to announce Gryffindor's newest member of the Quidditch team – our – (*she realises she can't be partial)* your superb new Chaser – Rose Granger-Weasley.

> *The Hall erupts into cheers.* SCORPIUS *claps alongside them all.*

ALBUS
Are you clapping her too? We hate Quidditch and she's playing for another house.

SCORPIUS
She's your cousin, Albus.

ALBUS
Do you think she'd clap for me?

SCORPIUS
I think she's brilliant.

> *The students circle* ALBUS *again as suddenly a Potions class begins.*

POLLY CHAPMAN
Albus Potter. An irrelevance. Even portraits turn the other way when he comes up the stairs.

> ALBUS *hunches over a potion.*

ALBUS
And now we add – is it horn of Bicorn?

KARL JENKINS
Leave him and Voldemort's child to it, I say.

ALBUS
With just a little salamander blood . . .

> *The potion explodes loudly.*

SCORPIUS
Okay. What's the counter-ingredient? What do we need to change?

ALBUS
Everything.

And with that, time moves ever onwards – ALBUS's *eyes become darker, his face grows more sallow. He's still an attractive boy, but he's trying not to admit it.*

And suddenly he's back on platform nine and three-quarters with his dad – who is still trying to persuade his son (and himself) that everything is okay. Both have aged another year.

HARRY

Third year. Big year. Here is your permission form for Hogsmeade.

ALBUS

I hate Hogsmeade.

HARRY

How can you hate a place you haven't actually visited yet?

ALBUS

Because I know it'll be full of Hogwarts students.

ALBUS *screws up the paper.*

HARRY

Just give it a go – come on – this is your chance to go nuts in Honeydukes without your mum knowing – no Albus, don't you dare.

ALBUS *(pointing his wand)*
Incendio!

The ball of paper bursts into flame, and ascends across the stage.

HARRY

Of all the stupid things!

ALBUS

The ironic thing is I didn't expect it to work. I'm terrible at that spell.

HARRY

Al–Albus, I've been exchanging owls with Professor
McGonagall – she says you're isolating yourself – you're
uncooperative in lessons – you're surly – you're—

ALBUS

So what would you like me to do? Magic myself popular?
Conjure myself into a new house? Transfigure myself into a
better student? Just cast a spell, Dad, and change me into
what you want me to be, okay? It'll work better for both of
us. Got to go. Train to catch. Friend to find.

> ALBUS *runs to* SCORPIUS, *who is sitting on his case – numb
> to the world.*

(*delighted*) Scorpius . . .

(*concerned*) Scorpius . . . are you okay?

> SCORPIUS *says nothing.* ALBUS *tries to read his friend's
> eyes.*

Your mum? It's got worse?

SCORPIUS

It's got the worst it can possibly get.

> ALBUS *sits down beside* SCORPIUS.

ALBUS

I thought you'd send an owl . . .

SCORPIUS

I couldn't work out what to say.

ALBUS

And now I don't know what to say . . .

SCORPIUS

Say nothing.

ALBUS

Is there anything . . .

SCORPIUS

Come to the funeral.

ALBUS

Of course.

SCORPIUS

And be my good friend.

> *And suddenly the* SORTING HAT *is centre stage and we're back in the Great Hall.*

SORTING HAT

Are you afraid of what you'll hear?
Afraid I'll speak the name you fear?
Not Slytherin! Not Gryffindor!
Not Hufflepuff! Not Ravenclaw!
Don't worry, child, I know my job,
You'll learn to laugh, if first you sob.
Lily Potter. GRYFFINDOR!

LILY

Yes!

ALBUS

Great.

SCORPIUS

Did you really think she'd come to us? Potters don't belong in Slytherin.

ALBUS

This one does.

> *As he tries to melt into the background, the other students laugh. He looks up at them all.*

I didn't choose, you know that? I didn't choose to be his son.

ACT ONE   SCENE FIVE

MINISTRY OF MAGIC, HARRY'S OFFICE

HERMIONE *sits with piles of paper in front of her in* HARRY's *messy office. She is slowly sorting through it all.* HARRY *enters in a rush. He is bleeding from a graze on his cheek.*

HERMIONE
How did it go?

HARRY
It was true.

HERMIONE
Theodore Nott?

HARRY
In custody.

HERMIONE
And the Time-Turner itself?

HARRY *reveals the Time-Turner. It shines out alluringly.*

Is it genuine? Does it work? It's not just an Hour-Reversal Turner – it goes back further?

HARRY
We don't know anything yet. I wanted to try it out there and then but wiser heads prevailed.

HERMIONE
Well, now we have it.

HARRY
And you're sure you want to keep it?

HERMIONE
I don't think we've a choice. Look at it. It's entirely different to the Time-Turner I had.

HARRY (*dryly*)
Apparently wizardry has moved on since we were kids.

HERMIONE
You're bleeding.

> HARRY *checks his face in the mirror. He dabs at the wound with his robes.*

Don't worry, it'll go with the scar.

HARRY (*with a grin*)
What you doing in my office, Hermione?

HERMIONE
I was anxious to hear about Theodore Nott and – thought I'd check whether you'd kept your promise and were on top of your paperwork.

HARRY
Ah. Turns out I'm not.

HERMIONE
No. You're not. Harry, how can you get any work done in this chaos?

> HARRY *waves his wand and the papers and books transform into neat piles.* HARRY *smiles.*

HARRY
No longer chaotic.

HERMIONE
But still ignored. You know there's some interesting stuff in here ... there are mountain trolls riding graphorns through

Hungary, there are giants with winged tattoos on their
backs walking through the Greek Seas, and the werewolves
have gone entirely underground—

HARRY

Great, let's get out there. I'll get the team together.

HERMIONE

Harry, I get it. Paperwork's boring . . .

HARRY

Not for you.

HERMIONE

I'm busy enough with my own. These are people and beasts
that fought alongside Voldemort in the great wizarding
wars. These are allies of darkness. This – combined
with what we have just unearthed at Theodore Nott's –
could mean something. But if the Head of Magical Law
Enforcement isn't reading his files—

HARRY

But I don't need to read it – I'm out there, hearing about it.
Theodore Nott – it was me who heard the rumours about
the Time-Turner and me who acted upon it. You really don't
need to tell me off.

HERMIONE *looks at* HARRY – *this is tricky.*

HERMIONE

Do you fancy a toffee? Don't tell Ron.

HARRY

You're changing the subject.

HERMIONE

I truly am. Toffee?

HARRY

Can't. We're off sugar at the moment.

Beat.

You know, you can get addicted to that stuff?

HERMIONE

What can I say? My parents were dentists, I was bound to
rebel at some point. Forty is leaving it a little late, but . . .
you've just done a brilliant thing. You're certainly not being
told off – I just need you to look at your paperwork every
now and again, that's all. Consider this a gentle – nudge –
from the *Minister for Magic.*

HARRY *hears the implication in her emphasis; he nods.*

How's Ginny? How's Albus?

HARRY

It seems I'm as good at fatherhood as I am at paperwork.
How's Rose? How's Hugo?

HERMIONE *(with a grin)*

You know, Ron says he thinks I see more of my secretary
Ethel *(she indicates off)* than him. Do you think there's a
point where we made a choice – parent of the year or –
Ministry official of the year? Go on. Go home to your
family Harry, the Hogwarts Express is about to depart for
another year – enjoy the time you've got left – and then
come back here with a fresh head and get these files
read.

HARRY

You really think this could all mean something?

HERMIONE *(with a smile)*

It could do. But if it does, we'll find a way to fight it, Harry.
We always have.

*She smiles once more – pops a toffee in her mouth and
leaves the office.* HARRY *is left alone. He packs his bag.
He walks out of the office and down a corridor. The
weight of the world upon his shoulders.*

He walks, tired, into a telephone box. He dials 62442.

PART ONE

TELEPHONE BOX
Farewell, Harry Potter.

He ascends away from the Ministry of Magic.

———————

ACT ONE   SCENE SIX

HARRY AND GINNY POTTER'S HOUSE

ALBUS *can't sleep. He is sitting at the top of the stairs. He hears voices below him. We hear* HARRY's *voice before he's revealed. An elderly man in a wheelchair is with him,* AMOS DIGGORY.

HARRY

Amos, I understand, I really do – but I'm only just home and—

AMOS

I've tried to make appointments at the Ministry. They say 'Ah, Mr Diggory, we have an appointment for you, let's see, in two months.' I wait. Very patiently.

HARRY

—and coming to my house in the middle of the night – when my kids are just getting ready for their new year at school – it's not right.

AMOS

Two months pass, I receive an owl, 'Mr Diggory, I'm awfully sorry, but Mr Potter has been called away on urgent business, we're going to have to shift things around a little, are you available for an appointment in, let's see, two months' time.' And then it repeats again, and again . . . You're shutting me out.

HARRY
Of course I'm not. It's just, I'm afraid, as Head of the
Department of Magical Law Enforcement I'm responsible—

AMOS
There's plenty you're responsible for.

HARRY
Sorry?

AMOS
My son, Cedric, you do remember Cedric, don't you?

HARRY *(remembering Cedric hurts him)*
Yes, I remember your son. His loss—

AMOS
Voldemort wanted *you*! Not my son! You told me yourself,
the words he said were 'kill the spare'. The spare. My son,
my beautiful son, was a spare.

HARRY
Mr Diggory, as you know, I sympathise with your efforts to
memorialise Cedric but—

AMOS
A memorial? I am not interested in a memorial – not any
more. I am an old man – an old, dying man – and I am here
to ask you – beg you – to help me get him back.

    HARRY *looks up, astonished.*

HARRY
Get him back? Amos, that's not possible.

AMOS
The Ministry has a Time-Turner does it not?

HARRY
The Time-Turners were all destroyed.

AMOS
The reason I'm here with such urgency is I've just heard
rumour – strong rumour – that the Ministry seized an

illegal Time-Turner from Theodore Nott and has kept it.
For investigation. Let me use that Time-Turner. Let me
have my son back.

There's a long, deadly pause. HARRY *is finding this extremely
difficult. We watch as* ALBUS *moves closer, listening.*

HARRY

Amos, playing with time? You know we can't do that.

AMOS

How many people have died for the Boy Who Lived? I'm
asking you to save one of them.

This hurts HARRY. *He thinks, his face hardens.*

HARRY

Whatever you've heard – the Theodore Nott story is a
fiction, Amos. I'm sorry.

DELPHI

Hello.

ALBUS *jumps a mile as* DELPHI – *a twenty-something
determined-looking woman – is revealed looking through
the stairs at him.*

Oh. Sorry. Didn't mean to startle. I used to be a big stair-
listener myself. Sitting there. Waiting for someone to say
something the tiniest bit interesting.

ALBUS

Who are you? Because this is sort of my house and ...

DELPHI

I'm a thief of course. I'm about to steal everything you own.
Give me your gold, your wand and your Chocolate Frogs!
(*She looks fierce and then smiles.*) Either that or I'm Delphini
Diggory. (*She ascends the stairs and sticks out a hand.*)
Delphi. I look after him – Amos – well, I try. (*She indicates*
AMOS.) And you are?

ALBUS *(rueful grin)*
  Albus.

DELPHI
  Of course! Albus Potter! So Harry is your dad? That's a bit
  wow isn't it?

ALBUS
  Not really.

DELPHI
  Ah. Have I just put my foot in it? It's what they used to say
  about me at school. Delphini Diggory – there isn't a hole
  she couldn't dig herself into.

ALBUS
  They do all sorts with my name too.

  Pause. She looks at him carefully.

AMOS
  Delphi.

  She makes to depart and then hesitates. She smiles at
  ALBUS.

DELPHI
  We don't choose who we're related to. Amos isn't just my
  patient, he's my uncle, it's part of the reason I took the job
  at Upper Flagley. But that's made it difficult. It's tough to
  live with people stuck in the past, isn't it?

AMOS
  Delphi!

ALBUS
  Upper Flagley?

DELPHI
  St Oswald's Home for Old Witches and Wizards. Come see
  us some time. If you like.

AMOS
  DELPHI!

She smiles and then trips as she travels down the stairs.
She enters the room with AMOS *and* HARRY *in it.* ALBUS
watches her.

DELPHI
Yes, Uncle?

AMOS
Meet the once-great Harry Potter, now a stone-cold
Ministry man. I will leave you in peace, sir. If peace is the
right word for it. Delphi, my chair . . .

DELPHI
Yes, Uncle.

AMOS *is pushed out of the room.* HARRY *is left, looking*
forlorn. ALBUS *watches on, thinking, carefully.*

ACT ONE   SCENE SEVEN

HARRY AND GINNY POTTER'S HOUSE, ALBUS'S ROOM

ALBUS *is sitting on the bed as the world goes on outside his door. Still against the constant motion outside. We hear a roar from* JAMES *(from off).*

GINNY

James, please, ignore your hair, and tidy that damn room . . .

JAMES

How can I ignore it? It's pink! I'm going to have to use my Invisibility Cloak!

JAMES *appears at the door, he has pink hair.*

GINNY

That's *not* why your dad gave you that cloak!

LILY

Who's seen my Potions book?

GINNY

Lily Potter, don't think you're wearing those to school tomorrow . . .

LILY *appears at* ALBUS's *door. She's wearing fairy wings that flutter.*

LILY

I love them. They're fluttery.

She exits as HARRY *appears in* ALBUS's *doorway. He looks through.*

HARRY

Hi.

There's an awkward pause between them. GINNY *appears in the doorway. She sees what's happening and stays a moment.*

Just delivering a pre-Hogwarts gift – gifts – Ron's sent this . . .

ALBUS

Okay, a love potion. Okay.

HARRY

I think it's a joke about – I don't know what. Lily got farting gnomes, James got a comb that's made his hair turn a shade of pink. Ron – well, Ron's Ron you know?

HARRY *puts down* ALBUS's *love potion on his bed.*

I also – this is from me . . .

He reveals a small blanket. GINNY *looks at it – she sees* HARRY *is trying, and then she softly walks away.*

ALBUS

An old blanket?

HARRY

I thought a lot about what to give you this year. James – well, James has been going on about the Invisibility Cloak since time itself, and Lily – I knew she'd love wings – but you. You're fourteen years old now, Albus, and I wanted to give you something which – meant something. This – is the last thing I had from my mum. The only thing. I was given to the Dursleys wrapped in it. I thought it had gone forever and then – when your Great Aunt Petunia died, hidden amongst her possessions, surprisingly, Dudley found this – and he kindly sent it on to me, and ever since then – well, any time I've wanted luck I've found it and just tried to hold it and I wondered if you . . .

ALBUS

Wanted to hold it too? Okay. Done. Let's hope it brings me luck. I certainly need some.

He touches the blanket.

But you should keep it.

HARRY

I think – believe – Petunia wanted me to have it, that's why she kept it and now I want you to have it from me. I didn't really know my mother – but I think she'd have wanted you to have it too. And maybe I could come find you – and it – on Hallows' Eve. I'd like to be with it on the night they died – and that could be good for the two of us . . .

ALBUS

Listen, I've got quite a lot of packing to do, and you undoubtedly have Ministry work coming out of your ears so . . .

HARRY

Albus, I want you to have the blanket.

ALBUS

And do what with it? Fairy wings make sense, Dad, Invisibility Cloaks, they also make sense – but this – really?

HARRY *is slightly heartbroken. He looks at his son, desperate to reach out.*

HARRY

Do you want a hand? Packing. I always loved packing. It meant I was leaving Privet Drive and going back to

Hogwarts. Which was ... well, I know you don't love it
but ...

ALBUS

For you, it's the greatest place on earth. I know. The poor
orphan, bullied by his Uncle and Aunt Dursley—

HARRY

Albus, please – can we just—

ALBUS

—traumatised by his cousin Dudley, saved by Hogwarts. I
know it all, Dad. Blah blah blah.

HARRY

I'm not going to rise to your bait, Albus Potter.

ALBUS

The poor orphan who went on to save us all – so may I
say – on behalf of wizarding kind. How grateful we are for
your heroism. Should we bow now or will a curtsey do?

HARRY

Albus, please – you know, I've never wanted gratitude.

ALBUS

But right now I'm overflowing with it – it must be the kind
gift of this mouldy blanket that did it ...

HARRY

Mouldy blanket?

ALBUS

What did you think would happen? We'd hug. I'd tell you I
always loved you. What? What?

HARRY (*finally losing his temper*)
You know what? I'm done with being made responsible
for your unhappiness. At least you've got a dad. Because I
didn't, okay?

ALBUS

And you think that was unlucky? I don't.

HARRY
You wish me dead?

ALBUS
No! I just wish you weren't my dad.

HARRY (*seeing red*)
Well, there are times I wish you weren't my son.

> *There's a silence.* ALBUS *nods. Pause.* HARRY *realises what he's said.*

No, I didn't mean that ...

ALBUS
Yes. You did.

HARRY
Albus, you just know how to get under my skin ...

ALBUS
You meant it, Dad. And, honestly, I don't blame you.

> *There's a horrible pause.*

You should probably leave me alone now.

HARRY
Albus, please ...

> ALBUS *picks up the blanket and throws it. It collides with Ron's love potion, which spills all over the blanket and the bed, producing a small puff of smoke.*

ALBUS
No luck or love for me, then.

> ALBUS *runs out of the room.* HARRY *goes after him.*

HARRY
Albus. Albus ... please ...

ACT ONE SCENE EIGHT

DREAM, HUT-ON-THE-ROCK

There's a LARGE BOOM. Then there's a LARGE CRASH. DUDLEY DURSLEY, AUNT PETUNIA *and* UNCLE VERNON *are cowering behind a bed.*

DUDLEY DURSLEY
Mum, I don't like this.

AUNT PETUNIA
I knew we made a mistake coming here. Vernon. Vernon. There's nowhere we can hide. Not even a lighthouse is far enough away!

There's another LARGE BOOM.

UNCLE VERNON
Hold on. Hold on. Whatever it is, it's not coming in here.

AUNT PETUNIA
We're cursed! He's cursed us! The boy has cursed us! (*Seeing* YOUNG HARRY.) This is all your fault. Get back in your hole.

YOUNG HARRY *flinches as* UNCLE VERNON *holds out his rifle.*

UNCLE VERNON
Whoever's there I should warn you – I'm armed.

There's a MASSIVE SMASH. And the door falls off its hinges. HAGRID *stands in the middle of the door. He looks at them all.*

HAGRID

Couldn't make us a cup o' tea, could yeh? It's not been an easy journey.

DUDLEY DURSLEY

Look. At. Him.

UNCLE VERNON

Stand back. Stand back. Behind me, Petunia. Behind me, Dudley. I'll soon see this scarramanger off.

HAGRID

Scarrawhat? (*He picks up* UNCLE VERNON's *gun.*) Haven't seen one of these for a while. (*He twists the end of the gun and ties it in a knot.*) Oops-a-daisy. (*And then he gets distracted. He's seen* YOUNG HARRY.) Harry Potter.

YOUNG HARRY

Hello.

HAGRID

Las' time I saw yeh, yeh was only a baby. Yeh look a lot like yer dad, but yeh've got yer mum's eyes.

YOUNG HARRY

You knew my parents?

HAGRID

Where's me manners? A very happy birthday to yeh. Got summat fer yeh here – I mighta sat on it at some point, but it'll taste all right.

From inside his coat he pulls a slightly squashed chocolate cake with 'Happy Birthday Harry' written on it in green icing.

YOUNG HARRY

Who are you?

HAGRID *(laughing)*
True, I haven't introduced meself. Rubeus Hagrid, Keeper of
Keys and Grounds at Hogwarts. *(He looks around himself.)*
What about that tea then, eh? I'd not say no ter summat
stronger if yeh've got it, mind.

YOUNG HARRY
Hogwhere?

HAGRID
Hogwarts. Yeh'll know all about Hogwarts, o' course.

YOUNG HARRY
Er – no. Sorry.

HAGRID
Sorry? It's them as should be sorry! I knew yeh weren't
gettin' yer letters but I never thought yeh wouldn't even
know abou' Hogwarts, fer cryin' out loud! Did yeh never
wonder where yer parents learnt it all?

YOUNG HARRY
Learnt what?

HAGRID *turns menacingly towards* UNCLE VERNON.

HAGRID
Do you mean ter tell me, that this boy – this boy! – knows
nothin' abou' – about ANYTHING?

UNCLE VERNON
I forbid you to tell the boy anything more!

YOUNG HARRY
Tell me what?

HAGRID *looks at* UNCLE VERNON *and then at* YOUNG
HARRY.

HAGRID
Harry – yer a wizard – yeh changed everything. Yer the
most famous wizard in the whole world.

And then right from the back of the room and whispering around everyone, words said with an unmistakeable voice. The voice of VOLDEMORT . . .
Haaarry Potttter . . .

ACT ONE   SCENE NINE

HARRY AND GINNY POTTER'S HOUSE, BEDROOM

HARRY *wakes suddenly. Breathing deeply in the night.*

He waits a moment. Calming himself. And then he feels intense pain, in his forehead. In his scar. Around him Dark Magic moves.

GINNY
> Harry . . .

HARRY
> It's fine. Go back to sleep.

GINNY
> Lumos.

> *The room is filled with light from her wand.* HARRY *looks at her.*

> A nightmare?

HARRY
> Yes.

GINNY
> About what?

HARRY
> The Dursleys – well it started there – then it became something else.

49

Pause. GINNY *looks at him – trying to work out where he is.*

GINNY

Do you want a Sleeping Draught?

HARRY

No. I'll be fine. Go back to sleep.

GINNY

You don't seem fine.

HARRY *says nothing.*

(*Seeing his agitation.*) It can't have been easy – with Amos Diggory.

HARRY

The anger I can cope with, the fact he's right is harder. Amos lost his son because of me—

GINNY

That doesn't seem particularly fair on yourself—

HARRY

—and there's nothing I can say – nothing I can say to anyone – unless it's the wrong thing of course.

GINNY *knows what – or rather who – he's referring to.*

GINNY

So that's what's upsetting you? The night before Hogwarts, it's never a good night if you don't want to go. Giving Al the blanket. It was a nice try.

HARRY

It went pretty badly wrong from there. I said some things Ginny . . .

GINNY

I heard.

HARRY

And you're still talking to me?

GINNY

Because I know that when the time is right you'll say sorry. That you didn't mean it. That what you said concealed – other things. You can be honest with him Harry . . . that's all he needs.

HARRY

I just wish he was more like James or Lily.

GINNY (*dryly*)

Yeah, maybe don't be that honest.

HARRY

No, I wouldn't change a thing about him . . . but I can understand them and . . .

GINNY

Albus is different and isn't that a good thing. And he can tell – you know – when you're putting on your Harry Potter front. He wants to see the real you.

HARRY

'The truth is a beautiful and terrible thing, and should therefore be treated with great caution.'

GINNY *looks at him, surprised.*

Dumbledore.

GINNY

A strange thing to say to a child.

HARRY

Not when you believe that child will have to die to save the world.

HARRY *gasps again – and does all he can not to touch his forehead.*

GINNY

Harry. What's wrong?

HARRY

Fine. I'm fine. I hear you. I'll try to be—

GINNY
    Does your scar hurt?

HARRY
    No. No. I'm fine. Now, Nox that and let's get some sleep.

GINNY
    Harry. How long has it been since your scar hurt?

    HARRY *turns to* GINNY, *his face says it all.*

HARRY
    Twenty-two years.

ACT ONE SCENE TEN

THE HOGWARTS EXPRESS

ALBUS *walks quickly along the train.*

ROSE
Albus, I've been looking for you . . .

ALBUS
Me? Why?

ROSE *isn't sure how to phrase what she has to say.*

ROSE
Albus, it's the start of the fourth year, and so the start of a
new year for us. I want to be friends again.

ALBUS
We never were friends.

ROSE
That's harsh! You were my best friend when I was six!

ALBUS
That was a long time ago.

*He makes to walk away, she pulls him into an empty
compartment.*

ROSE
Have you heard the rumours? Big Ministry raid a few days
ago. Your dad apparently was incredibly brave.

ALBUS

How do you always know about these things and I don't?

ROSE

Apparently he – the wizard they raided – Theodore Nott I think – had all sorts of artefacts that broke all sorts of laws including – and this has got them all gooey – an illegal Time-Turner. And quite a superior one at that.

ALBUS *looks at* ROSE, *everything falling into place.*

ALBUS

A Time-Turner? My dad found a Time-Turner?

ROSE

Sh! Yes. I know. Great, right?

ALBUS

You're sure.

ROSE

Entirely.

ALBUS

Now I have to find Scorpius.

He walks down the train. ROSE *follows, still determined to say her piece.*

ROSE

Albus!

ALBUS *turns decisively.*

ALBUS

Who's told you that you have to talk to me?

ROSE *(sprung)*

Okay, maybe your mum owled my dad – but only because she's worried about you. And I just think—

ALBUS

Leave me alone, Rose.

SCORPIUS *is sitting in his usual compartment.* ALBUS *enters first,* ROSE *still tailing him.*

SCORPIUS
Albus! Oh hello Rose, what do you smell of?

ROSE
What do I *smell* of?

SCORPIUS
No, I meant it as a nice thing. You smell like a mixture of fresh flowers and fresh – bread.

ROSE
Albus, I'm here, okay? If you need me.

SCORPIUS
I mean, nice bread, good bread, bread . . . what's wrong with bread?

ROSE *walks away, shaking her head.*

ROSE
What's wrong with bread!

ALBUS
I've been looking for you everywhere . . .

SCORPIUS
And now you've found me. Tada! I was hardly hiding. You know how I like to . . . get on early. Stops people staring. Shouting. Writing 'son of Voldemort' on my trunk. That one never gets old. She really doesn't like me does she?

ALBUS *hugs his friend. With fierceness. They hold for a beat.* SCORPIUS *is surprised by this.*

Okay. Hello. Um. Have we hugged before? Do we hug?

The two boys awkwardly dislocate.

ALBUS
Just a slightly weird twenty-four hours.

55

SCORPIUS

What's happened in them?

ALBUS

I'll explain later. We have to get off this train.

There's the sound of whistles from off. The train starts moving.

SCORPIUS

Too late. The train is moving. Hogwarts ahoy!

ALBUS

Then we have to get off a moving train.

TROLLEY WITCH

Anything from the trolley, dears?

ALBUS *opens a window and makes to climb out.*

SCORPIUS

A moving magical train.

TROLLEY WITCH

Pumpkin Pasty? Cauldron Cake?

SCORPIUS

Albus Severus Potter, get that strange look out of your eye.

ALBUS

First question. What do you know about the Triwizard Tournament?

SCORPIUS *(happy)*

Ooooh, a quiz! Three schools pick three champions to compete in three tasks for one Cup. What's that got to do with anything?

ALBUS

You really are an enormous geek you know that?

SCORPIUS

Ya-huh.

ALBUS

Second question. Why has the Triwizard Tournament not been run in over twenty years?

SCORPIUS

The last competition included your dad and a boy called
Cedric Diggory – they decided to win together but the Cup
was a Portkey – and they were transported to Voldemort.
Cedric was killed. They cancelled the competition
immediately after.

ALBUS

Good. Third question. Did Cedric need to be killed? Easy
question, easy answer: No. The words Voldemort said were
'kill the spare'. The spare. He died only because he was
with my father and my father couldn't save him – we can.
A mistake has been made and we're going to right it. We're
going to use a Time-Turner. We're going to bring him back.

SCORPIUS

Albus, for obvious reasons, I'm not a massive fan of
Time-Turners . . .

ALBUS

When Amos Diggory asked for the Time-Turner my father
denied they even existed. He lied to an old man who just
wanted his son back – who just loved his son. And he did it
because he didn't care . . . because he doesn't care. Everyone
talks about all the brave things Dad did. But he made some
mistakes too. Some big mistakes, in fact. I want to set one
of those mistakes right. I want us to save Cedric.

SCORPIUS

Okay, whatever was holding your brain together seems to
have snapped.

ALBUS

I'm going to do this, Scorpius. I need to do this. And you
know as well as I do, I'll entirely mess it up if you don't
come with me. Come on.

He grins. And then disappears ever up. SCORPIUS
*hesitates for a moment. He makes a face. And then
hoists himself up and disappears after* ALBUS.

ACT ONE SCENE ELEVEN

THE HOGWARTS EXPRESS, ROOF

The wind whistles from all angles and it's a fierce wind at that.

SCORPIUS

Okay, now we're on the roof of a train, it's fast, it's scary, this has been great, I feel like I've learnt a lot about me, something about you, but—

ALBUS

As I calculate it we should be approaching the viaduct soon and then it'll be a short hike to St Oswald's Home for Old Witches and Wizards . . .

SCORPIUS

The what? The where? Look, I am as excited as you are to be a rebel for the first time in my life – yay – train roof – fun – but now – oh.

SCORPIUS *sees something he doesn't want to see.*

ALBUS

The water will be an extremely useful back-up if our Cushioning Charm doesn't work.

SCORPIUS

Albus. The Trolley Witch.

ALBUS

You want a snack for the journey?

SCORPIUS

No. Albus. The Trolley Witch is coming towards us.

ALBUS

No, she can't be, we're on top of the train . . .

> SCORPIUS *points* ALBUS *in the right direction, and*
> *now he can see the* TROLLEY WITCH, *who approaches*
> *nonchalantly. Pushing her trolley.*

TROLLEY WITCH

Anything from the trolley, dears? Pumpkin Pasty?
Chocolate Frog? Cauldron Cake?

ALBUS

Oh.

TROLLEY WITCH

People don't know much about me. They buy my Cauldron
Cakes – but they never really notice me. I don't remember
the last time someone asked my name.

ALBUS

What is your name?

TROLLEY WITCH

I've forgotten. All I can tell you is that when the Hogwarts
Express first came to be – Ottaline Gambol herself offered
me this job . . .

SCORPIUS

That's – a hundred and ninety years. You've been doing this
job for a hundred and ninety years?

TROLLEY WITCH

These hands have made over six million Pumpkin Pasties.
I've got quite good at them. But what people haven't
noticed about my Pumpkin Pasties is how easily they
transform into something else . . .

*She picks up a Pumpkin Pasty. She throws it like a
grenade. It explodes.*

And you won't believe what I can do with my Chocolate
Frogs. Never. Never. Have I let anyone off this train before
they reached their destination. Some have tried – Sirius
Black and his cronies, Fred and George Weasley. ALL
HAVE FAILED. BECAUSE THIS TRAIN – IT DOESN'T
LIKE PEOPLE GETTING OFF IT . . .

*The TROLLEY WITCH's hands transfigure into very sharp
spikes. She smiles.*

So please retake your seats for the remainder of the journey.

ALBUS
You were right, Scorpius. This train is magical.

SCORPIUS
At this precise moment in time, I take no pleasure in being
right.

ALBUS
But I was also right – about the viaduct – that's water down
there, time to try the Cushioning Charm.

SCORPIUS
Albus, this is a bad idea.

ALBUS
Is it? (*He has a moment's hesitation, then he realises the time
for hesitation has passed.*) Too late now. Three. Two. One.
Molliare!

He incants as he jumps.

SCORPIUS
Albus . . . Albus . . .

*He looks down desperately after his friend. He looks
at the approaching TROLLEY WITCH. Her hair wild. Her
spikes particularly spiky.*

Well, as fun as you clearly look, I have to go after my friend.

He pinches his nose, he jumps after ALBUS, *incanting as he goes.*

Molliare!

ACT ONE   SCENE TWELVE

MINISTRY OF MAGIC, GRAND MEETING ROOM

The stage is flooded with wizards and witches. They rattle and chatter like all true wizards and witches can. Amongst them, GINNY, DRACO and RON. Above them, on a stage, HERMIONE and HARRY.

HERMIONE
Order. Order. Do I have to conjure silence? (*She pulls silence from the crowd using her wand.*) Good. Welcome to this Extraordinary General Meeting. I'm so pleased so many of you could make it. The wizarding world has been living in peace now for many years. It's twenty-two years since we defeated Voldemort at the Battle of Hogwarts and I'm delighted to say there is a new generation being brought up having known only the slightest conflict. Until now. Harry?

HARRY
Voldemort's allies have been showing movement for a few months now. We've followed trolls making their way across Europe, giants starting to cross the seas, and the werewolves – well, I'm distressed to say we lost sight of them some weeks ago. We don't know where they're going or who's encouraged them to move – but we are aware they are moving – and we are concerned what it might mean. So

we're asking – if anyone has seen anything? Felt anything?
If you could raise a wand, we will hear everyone speak.
Professor McGonagall – thank you.

PROFESSOR McGONAGALL

It did look like the Potions stores had been interfered with
when we returned from summer break, but not a huge
amount of ingredients were missing, some Boomslang skin
and lacewing flies, nothing on the Restricted Register. We
put it down to Peeves.

HERMIONE

Thank you, Professor. We shall investigate. (*She looks
around the room.*) Nobody else? Fine, and – gravest of all –
and this hasn't been the case since Voldemort – Harry's
scar is hurting again.

DRACO

Voldemort is dead, Voldemort is gone.

HERMIONE

Yes, Draco, Voldemort is dead but these things all lead us
to think that there is a possibility that Voldemort – or some
trace of Voldemort – might be back.

   This gets a reaction.

HARRY

Now this is difficult but we have to ask it to rule it out.
Those of you with a Dark Mark . . . have you felt anything?
Even a twinge?

DRACO

Back to being prejudiced against those with a Dark Mark
are we, Potter?

HERMIONE

No, Draco. Harry is simply trying to—

DRACO

You know what this is about? Harry just wants his face back
in the newspapers again. We've had rumours of Voldemort

coming back from the *Daily Prophet* once a year every
year—

HARRY

None of those rumours came from me!

DRACO

Really? Doesn't your wife edit the *Daily Prophet*?

GINNY *steps towards him, outraged.*

GINNY

The sports pages!

HERMIONE

Draco. Harry brought this matter to the attention of the
Ministry . . . and I, as Minister for Magic—

DRACO

A vote you only won because you are his friend.

RON *is held back by* GINNY *as he charges at* DRACO.

RON

Do you want a smack in the mouth?

DRACO

Face it – his celebrity impacts upon you all. And how better
to get everyone whispering the Potter name again than
with *(he does an impression of* HARRY*)* 'my scar is hurting, my
scar is hurting'. And do you know what this all means –
that the gossipmongers once again have an opportunity
to defame my son with these ridiculous rumours about his
parentage.

HARRY

Draco, no one is saying this has anything to do with
Scorpius . . .

DRACO

Well, I, for one, think this meeting a sham. And I'm
leaving.

He walks out. Others start to disperse after him.

HERMIONE
    No. That's not the way . . . come back. We need a strategy.

ACT ONE   SCENE THIRTEEN

ST OSWALD'S HOME FOR OLD WITCHES AND WIZARDS

This is chaos. This is magic. This is St Oswald's Home for Old Witches and Wizards and it is as wonderful as you might hope.

Zimmer frames are conjured into life, knitting wool is enchanted into chaos, and male nurses are made to dance the tango.

These are people relieved of the burden of having to do magic for a reason – instead, these witches and wizards do magic for fun. And what fun they have.

ALBUS *and* SCORPIUS *enter, looking around themselves, amused, and – let's face it – slightly scared.*

ALBUS *and* SCORPIUS
 Um, excuse me ... Excuse me. EXCUSE ME!

SCORPIUS
 Okay, so this place is wild.

ALBUS
 We're looking for Amos Diggory.

 There is suddenly total silence. Everything is instantly still. And slightly depressed.

WOOL WOMAN
 And what'you boys want with that miserable old sod?

66

DELPHI *appears with a smile.*

DELPHI

Albus? Albus! You came? How wonderful! Come and say hello to Amos!

ACT ONE   SCENE FOURTEEN

ST OSWALD'S HOME FOR OLD WITCHES AND WIZARDS, AMOS'S ROOM

AMOS *looks at* SCORPIUS *and* ALBUS, *irritated.* DELPHI *watches the three of them.*

AMOS

So let me get this straight. You overhear a conversation – a conversation which was not meant for you to overhear – and you decide, without prompting – in fact, without leave – to interfere, and interfere hard, in someone else's business.

ALBUS

My father lied to you – I know he did – they do have a Time-Turner.

AMOS

Of course they do. You can move along now.

ALBUS

What? No. We're here to help.

AMOS

Help? What use could a pair of undersized teenagers be for me?

ALBUS

My father proved you don't have to be grown up to change the wizarding world.

AMOS

So I should allow you to get involved because you're a Potter? Relying on your famous name are you?

ALBUS

No!

AMOS

A Potter who is in Slytherin house – yes, I've read about you – and who brings a Malfoy with him to visit me – a Malfoy who may be a Voldemort? Who's to say you're not involved in Dark Magic?

ALBUS

But—

AMOS

Your information was obvious but the confirmation is useful. Your father did lie. Now leave. The pair of you. And stop wasting my time.

ALBUS (*with power and strength*)

No, you need to listen to me, you said it yourself – how much blood is on my father's hands. Let me help you change that. Let me help correct one of his mistakes. Trust me.

AMOS (*his voice raised*)

Did you not hear me, boy? I see no reason to trust you. So go. Now. Before I *make* you leave.

He raises his wand ominously. ALBUS *looks at the wand – he deflates –* AMOS *has crushed him.*

SCORPIUS

Come on mate, if there's one thing we're good at, it's knowing where we're not wanted.

ALBUS *is reluctant to leave.* SCORPIUS *pulls him by the arm. He turns and they walk away.*

DELPHI

I can think of one reason why you should trust them,
Uncle.

They stop.

They're the only ones volunteering to help. They're
prepared to bravely put themselves at risk to return your son
to your side. In fact, I'm pretty sure they put themselves at
risk even getting here . . .

AMOS

This is Cedric we're talking about . . .

DELPHI

And – didn't you say yourself – having someone inside
Hogwarts might be a *massive* advantage?

> DELPHI *kisses the top of* AMOS's *head.* AMOS *looks at*
> DELPHI, *and then turns to look at the boys.*

AMOS

Why? Why do you want to put yourself at risk? What's in it
for you?

ALBUS

I know what it is to be the spare. Your son didn't deserve to
be killed, Mr Diggory. We can help you get him back.

AMOS *(finally showing emotion)*

My son – my son was the best thing that ever happened to
me – and you're right it was an injustice – a gross injustice –
if you're serious . . .

ALBUS

We're deadly serious.

AMOS

This is going to be dangerous.

ALBUS

We know.

SCORPIUS
Do we?

AMOS
Delphi – perhaps if you were prepared to accompany them?

DELPHI
If that would make you happy, Uncle.

She smiles at ALBUS, *he smiles back.*

AMOS
You do understand even getting the Time-Turner will risk your lives.

ALBUS
We're ready to put our lives at risk.

SCORPIUS
Are we?

AMOS (*gravely*)
I hope you have it in you.

ACT ONE SCENE FIFTEEN

HARRY AND GINNY POTTER'S HOUSE, KITCHEN

HARRY, RON, HERMIONE *and* GINNY *sit eating together.*

HERMIONE

I've told Draco again and again – no one in the Ministry is saying anything about Scorpius. The rumours aren't coming from us.

GINNY

I wrote to him – after he lost Astoria – to ask if there's anything we could do. I thought maybe – as he was such a good friend to Albus – maybe Scorpius might want to stay over part of the Christmas break or ... My owl came back with a letter containing one simple sentence: 'Tell your husband to refute these allegations about my son once and for all.'

HERMIONE

He's obsessed.

GINNY

He's a mess – a grieving mess.

RON

And I'm sorry for his loss, but when he accuses Hermione of ... well ... (*he looks across at* HARRY) Oi droopy drawers, like I say to her all the time, it could be nothing.

72

HERMIONE

Her?

RON

The trolls could be going to a party, the giants to a
wedding, you could be getting bad dreams because you're
worried about Albus, and your scar could be hurting
because you're getting old.

HARRY

Getting old? Thanks, mate.

RON

Honestly, every time I sit down now I make an 'ooof' noise.
An 'ooof'. And my feet – the trouble I'm having with my
feet – I could write songs about the pain my feet give me –
maybe your scar is like that.

GINNY

You talk a lot of rubbish.

RON

I consider it my speciality. That and my range of Skiving
Snackboxes. And my love for all of you. Even Skinny
Ginny.

GINNY

If you don't behave, Ronald Weasley, I will tell Mum.

RON

You wouldn't.

HERMIONE

If some part of Voldemort survived, in whatever form, we
need to be prepared. And I'm scared.

GINNY

I'm scared too.

RON

Nothing scares me. Apart from Mum.

HERMIONE

I mean it, Harry, I will not be Cornelius Fudge on this one.

I will not stick my head in the sand. And I don't care how unpopular that makes me with Draco Malfoy.

RON
You never really were one for popularity were you?

> HERMIONE *shoots* RON *a withering look as she aims to hit him but* RON *jumps out of the way.*

Missed.

> GINNY *hits* RON. RON *winces.*

Hit. A very solid hit.

> *Suddenly an owl is in the room. It swoops in low and drops a letter on Harry's plate.*

HERMIONE
Bit late for an owl isn't it?

> *Harry opens the letter. Surprised.*

HARRY
It's from Professor McGonagall.

GINNY
What does it say?

> HARRY'S *face drops.*

HARRY
Ginny, it's Albus – Albus and Scorpius – they never made it to school. They're missing!

ACT ONE   SCENE SIXTEEN

WHITEHALL, CELLAR

SCORPIUS *is squinting at a bottle.*

SCORPIUS
So we just take it?

ALBUS
Scorpius, do I really need to explain to you – uber geek and
Potions expert – what Polyjuice does? Thanks to Delphi's
brilliant preparation work, we are going to take this potion
and be transformed, and thus disguised we will be able to
enter the Ministry of Magic.

SCORPIUS
Okay, two points, one, is it painful?

DELPHI
Very – as I understand it.

SCORPIUS
Thank you. Good to know. Second point – do either of you
know what Polyjuice tastes of? Because I've heard it tastes
of fish, and if it does I will just vomit it back up. Fish doesn't
agree with me. Never has. Never will.

DELPHI
Consider us warned. (*She knocks back the potion.*) It doesn't
taste of fish. (*She begins to transform. It's agonising.*) Actually

75

it tastes quite pleasant, yum. It is painful but . . . (*She burps, loudly.*) Take it back. There is a – slight – (*She burps again and turns into* HERMIONE.) Slight – overpowering – fishy residue.

ALBUS
Okay, that's – wow!

SCORPIUS
Double wow!

DELPHI/HERMIONE
This really doesn't feel how I – I even sound like her! Triple wow!

ALBUS
Right. Me next.

SCORPIUS
No. No way, José. If we're doing this, we're doing it (*he puts on a pair of familiar-looking glasses with a smile*) together.

ALBUS
Three. Two. One.

They swallow.

No, that's good (*he's racked with pain*). That's less good.

They both start to transform and it's agonising.

ALBUS *turns into* RON, SCORPIUS *into* HARRY.

The two look at each other. There's a silence.

ALBUS/RON
This is going to be slightly weird isn't it?

SCORPIUS/HARRY (*full of drama – he's really enjoying this*)
Go to your room. Go straight to your room. You've been an incredibly awful and bad son.

ALBUS/RON (*with a laugh*)
Scorpius . . .

SCORPIUS/HARRY *(tossing his cloak over his shoulder)*
It was your idea – I be him and you be Ron! I just want
to have a little fun before I ... *(And then he burps loudly.)*
Okay, so that's utterly horrible.

ALBUS/RON
You know, he hides it well, but Uncle Ron's got a bit of a
gut growing.

DELPHI/HERMIONE
We should go – don't you think?

> *They emerge on to the street. They enter a telephone box.*
> *They dial 62442.*

TELEPHONE BOX
Welcome, Harry Potter. Welcome, Hermione Granger.
Welcome, Ron Weasley.

> *They smile as the telephone box disappears into the floor.*

ACT ONE   SCENE SEVENTEEN

MINISTRY OF MAGIC, MEETING ROOM

HARRY, HERMIONE, GINNY *and* DRACO *pace around a small room.*

DRACO
Have we searched thoroughly beside the tracks . . .

HARRY
My department have searched once and are searching
again.

DRACO
And the Trolley Witch is not able to tell us anything useful?

HERMIONE
The Trolley Witch is furious. She keeps talking about
letting down Ottaline Gambol. She prides herself on her
Hogwarts delivery record.

GINNY
Have there been any instances of magic reported by the
Muggles?

HERMIONE
None so far. I have made the Muggle Prime Minister aware
and he is filing what is known as a misper. Sounds like a
spell. It isn't.

DRACO

So now we're relying on Muggles to find our children? Have we told them about Harry's scar too?

HERMIONE

We're merely asking the Muggles to help. And who knows how Harry's scar might be involved but it's certainly a matter we're taking seriously. Our Aurors are currently investigating anyone involved in Dark Magic and—

DRACO

This is not Death Eater-related.

HERMIONE

I'm not sure I share your confidence . . .

DRACO

I'm not confident, I'm right. The sort of cretins pursuing Dark Magic now. My son is a Malfoy, they wouldn't dare.

HARRY

Unless there's something new out there, something to—

GINNY

I agree with Draco – if this is a kidnap – taking Albus I understand, taking them both . . .

HARRY *locks eyes with* GINNY, *it becomes clear what she wants him to say.*

DRACO

And Scorpius is a follower not a leader despite everything I've tried to instil in him. So it's undoubtedly Albus who got him from that train and my question is, where would he take him?

GINNY

Harry, they've run away, you and I know it.

DRACO *notices the couple staring at each other.*

DRACO

Do you? Know it? What aren't you telling us?

There's a silence.

Whatever information you're concealing, I recommend you share it now.

HARRY
Albus and I had an argument, the day before last.

DRACO
And ...

> HARRY *hesitates and then makes brave eye contact with* DRACO.

HARRY
And I told him that there were times when I wished he weren't my son.

There's another silence. A profoundly powerful one. And then DRACO *takes a dangerous step towards* HARRY.

DRACO
If anything happens to Scorpius ...

> GINNY *steps in between* DRACO *and* HARRY.

GINNY
Don't throw around threats Draco, please don't do that.

DRACO *(roar)*
My son is missing!

GINNY *(an equal roar)*
So is mine!

He meets her look. There's real emotion in this room.

DRACO *(lip curling, every inch his father)*
If you need gold ... everything the Malfoys have ... he's my sole heir ... he's my – only family.

HERMIONE
The Ministry has plenty in reserve, thank you Draco.

DRACO *makes to leave. He stops. He looks at* HARRY.

DRACO
I don't care what you did or who you saved, you are a constant curse on my family, Harry Potter.

ACT ONE   SCENE EIGHTEEN

MINISTRY OF MAGIC, CORRIDOR

SCORPIUS/HARRY
And you're sure it's in there?

A GUARD *walks past.* SCORPIUS/HARRY *and* DELPHI/
HERMIONE *try to affect performances.*

Yes Minister, I definitely think this is a matter for the
Ministry to ponder at length, yes.

GUARD (*with a nod*)
Minister.

DELPHI/HERMIONE
Let's ponder it together.

The GUARD *walks on, they let out a sigh of relief.*

It was my uncle's idea to use the Veritaserum – we slipped it
into a visiting Ministry official's drink. He told us that the
Time-Turner had been kept and even told us where – the
office of the Minister for Magic herself.

She indicates a door. Suddenly they hear a noise.

HERMIONE (*from off*)
Harry ... we should talk about it ...

HARRY *(from off)*
    There's nothing to talk about.

DELPHI/HERMIONE
    Oh no.

ALBUS/RON
    Hermione. And Dad.

    The panic is instant and infectious.

SCORPIUS/HARRY
    Okay. Hiding places. No hiding places. Anyone know any
    Invisibility Charms?

DELPHI/HERMIONE
    Do we go – in her office?

ALBUS/RON
    She'll be coming to her office.

DELPHI/HERMIONE
    There's nowhere else.

    She tries the door. She tries it again.

HERMIONE *(from off)*
    If you don't talk to me or Ginny about it . . .

SCORPIUS/HARRY
    Stand back. Alohomora!

    *He aims his wand at the door. The door swings open. He
    grins – delighted.*

    Albus. Block her. It has to be you.

HARRY *(from off)*
    What is there to say?

ALBUS/RON
    Me. Why?

DELPHI/HERMIONE
    Well, it can't be either of us can it? We *are* them.

HERMIONE *(from off)*
> What you said was obviously wrong – but – there are more factors at play here than—

ALBUS/RON
> But I can't ... I can't ...

> *There's a small kerfuffle and then* ALBUS/RON *ends up standing outside the door as* HERMIONE *and* HARRY *enter from off.*

HARRY
> Hermione, I'm grateful for your concern but there's no need—

HERMIONE
> Ron?

ALBUS/RON
> Surprise!!!

HERMIONE
> What are you doing here?

ALBUS/RON
> Does a man need an excuse to see his wife?

> *He kisses* HERMIONE *firmly.*

HARRY
> I should go ...

HERMIONE
> Harry. My point is whatever Draco says – the things you said to Albus ... I don't think it'll do any of us any good for you to dwell on it ...

ALBUS/RON
> Oh, you're talking about how Harry said sometimes he wished I— *(he corrects himself)* Albus weren't his son.

HERMIONE
> Ron!

ALBUS/RON
Better out than in, that's what I say . . .

HERMIONE
He'll know . . . we all say stuff we don't mean. He knows that.

ALBUS/RON
But what if sometimes we say stuff we do mean . . . what then?

HERMIONE
Ron, now's not the time, honestly.

ALBUS/RON
Of course it isn't. Bye, bye darling.

> ALBUS/RON *watches her go, hopeful she'll walk past her office and away. But of course she doesn't. He runs to block her before she enters through her door. He blocks her once, and then blocks her again, swinging his hips to do so.*

HERMIONE
Why are you blocking the entrance to my office?

ALBUS/RON
I'm not. Blocking. Anything.

> *She again makes for the door, he blocks her again.*

HERMIONE
You are. Let me into my room, Ron.

ALBUS/RON
Let's have another baby.

> HERMIONE *tries to dodge past him.*

HERMIONE
What?

ALBUS/RON
Or if not another baby, a holiday. I want a baby or a holiday

and I'm going to insist on it. Shall we talk about it later, honey?

She tries to get into the room one final time, he blocks her with a kiss. It develops into quite a struggle.

Maybe with a drink in the Leaky Cauldron? Love you.

HERMIONE *(relenting)*
If there's another stink pellet in there then Merlin won't help you. Fine. We're due to update the Muggles anyway.

She exits. HARRY exits with her.

ALBUS/RON turns towards the door. She re-enters, this time, alone.

A baby – OR – a holiday? Some days you are off the scale you know that?

ALBUS/RON
It's why you married me isn't it? My puckish sense of fun.

She exits again. He starts to open the door but again she re-enters, he slams it closed.

HERMIONE
I can taste fish. I told you to stay away from those fish finger sandwiches.

ALBUS/RON
Right you are.

She exits. He checks she's gone and the relief floods out of him as he opens the door.

ACT ONE   SCENE NINETEEN

MINISTRY OF MAGIC, HERMIONE'S OFFICE

SCORPIUS/HARRY *and* DELPHI/HERMIONE *are waiting on the other side of* HERMIONE's *office door as* ALBUS/RON *enters – he slumps, exhausted.*

ALBUS/RON
This is all too weird.

DELPHI/HERMIONE
You were impressive. Good blocking action.

SCORPIUS/HARRY
I don't know whether to high-five you or frown at you for kissing your aunt about five hundred times!

ALBUS/RON
Ron's an affectionate guy. I was trying to distract her, Scorpius. I did distract her.

SCORPIUS/HARRY
And then there's what your dad said . . .

DELPHI/HERMIONE
Boys . . . she will be back – we don't have long.

ALBUS/RON (*to* SCORPIUS/HARRY)
You heard that?

DELPHI/HERMIONE
Where would Hermione hide a Time-Turner? (*She looks*

around the room and sees the bookcases.) Search the bookcases.

They start to search. SCORPIUS/HARRY *looks at his friend, concerned.*

SCORPIUS/HARRY
Why didn't you tell me?

ALBUS/RON
My dad says he wishes I weren't his son. Hardly a conversation starter is it?

SCORPIUS/HARRY *tries to work out what to say.*

SCORPIUS/HARRY
I know the – Voldemort thing isn't – true – and – you know – but sometimes, I think I can see my dad thinking: how did I produce this?

ALBUS/RON
Still better than my dad. I'm pretty sure he spends most of his time thinking: how can I give him back?

DELPHI/HERMIONE *tries to pull* SCORPIUS/HARRY *towards the bookcases.*

DELPHI/HERMIONE
Maybe if we could concentrate on the matter at hand.

SCORPIUS/HARRY
My point is – there's a reason – we're friends, Albus – a reason we found each other, you know? And whatever this – adventure is about . . .

Then he spots a book on the shelf that makes him frown.

Have you seen the books on these shelves? There are some serious books here. Banned books. Cursed books.

ALBUS/RON

How to distract Scorpius from difficult emotional issues.
Take him to a library.

SCORPIUS/HARRY

All the books from the Restricted Section and then some.
*Magick Moste Evile, Fifteenth-Century Fiends. Sonnets of a
Sorcerer* – that's not even allowed in Hogwarts!

ALBUS/RON

Shadows and Spirits. The Nightshade Guide to Necromancy.

DELPHI/HERMIONE

They are quite something aren't they . . .

ALBUS/RON

*The True History of the Opal Fire. The Imperius Curse and
How to Abuse it.*

SCORPIUS/HARRY

And lookee here. Whoah. *My Eyes and How to See Past
Them* by Sybill Trelawney. A book on divination. Hermione
Granger hates divination. This is fascinating. This is a
find . . .

*He pulls the book from the shelf. And it falls open. And
speaks.*

BOOK

The first is the fourth, a disappointing mark
You'll find it in parked but not in park.

SCORPIUS/HARRY

Okay. A book that talks. Bit weird.

BOOK

The second is the less fair of those that walk on two legs.
Grubby, hairy a disease of the egg.
And the third is both a mountain to climb and a route to
take.

ALBUS/RON

It's a riddle. It's giving us a riddle.

BOOK
> A turn in the city, a glide through a lake.

DELPHI/HERMIONE
> What have you done?

SCORPIUS/HARRY
> I, uh, I opened a book. Something which has – in all my years on this planet – never been a particularly dangerous activity.

> *The books reach out and grab* ALBUS. *He only just eludes their grasp.*

ALBUS/RON
> What is that?

DELPHI/HERMIONE
> She's weaponised it. She's weaponised her library. This is where the Time-Turner will be. Solve the riddle and we'll find it.

ALBUS/RON
> The first is a fourth. You'll find it in parked, not in park. Ed – De—

> *The books start to try and swallow* DELPHI/HERMIONE.

SCORPIUS/HARRY
> The second is a disease of the egg, the less fair of those who walk on two legs ...

DELPHI/HERMIONE (*effusively*)
> Men! De – men – tors. We need to find a book on Dementors (*the bookcase pulls her in*), Albus!

ALBUS/RON
> Delphi! What is going on?

SCORPIUS/HARRY
> Concentrate, Albus. Do what she said. Find a book on Dementors and be very careful.

ALBUS/RON
> Here. *Dominating Dementors: A True History of Azkaban.*

> *The book flies open and swings dangerously at* SCORPIUS/
> HARRY, *who has to dodge out of the way. He falls hard
> against a bookcase which attempts to consume him.*

BOOK
> I was born in a cage
> But smashed it with rage
> The Gaunt inside me
> Riddled me free
> Of that which would stop me to be.

ALBUS/RON
> Voldemort.

> DELPHI *plunges through the books, back as herself.*

DELPHI
> Work faster!

> *She's pulled back in screaming.*

ALBUS/RON
> Delphi! Delphi!

> *He tries to grab her hand, but she's gone.*

SCORPIUS/HARRY
> She'd become herself again – did you notice?

ALBUS/RON
> No! Because I was more worried about her being eaten by a
> bookcase! Find. Something. Anything on him.

> *He finds a book.*

> *The Heir of Slytherin? Do you think?*

> *He pulls the book from the shelf, it pulls back,* ALBUS/RON
> *is consumed by the bookcase.*

SCORPIUS/HARRY
Albus? Albus!!

But ALBUS/RON *is gone.*

Okay. Not that. Voldemort. Voldemort. Voldemort.

He scans the shelves.

Marvolo: The Truth, this must be ...

*He pulls it open. Again it swings away, revealing a
splintering light, and a deeper voice than previously
heard.*

BOOK
I am the creature you have not seen
I am you. I am me. The echo unforeseen.
Sometimes in front, sometimes behind,
A constant companion, for we are entwined.

ALBUS *emerges from the books. As himself again.*

SCORPIUS/HARRY
Albus ...

He tries to grab him.

ALBUS
No. Just – THIIIIINK.

ALBUS *is violently pulled back into the bookcase.*

SCORPIUS/HARRY
But I can't ... an invisible echo, what is that? The only
thing I'm good at is thinking and when I need to think – I
can't.

*The books pull him inside them; he's powerless. This is
terrifying.*
There's silence.

Then BANG – a shower of books are released from the bookcase – and SCORPIUS *re-emerges. Smashing the books aside.*

SCORPIUS

No! You don't! Sybill Trelawney. No!!!

He looks around, sunk but full of energy.

This is all wrong. Albus? Can you hear me? All this for a frigging Time-Turner. Think, Scorpius. Think.

Books try and grab him.

A constant companion. Sometimes behind. Sometimes in front. Hang on. I've missed it. Shadow. You're a shadow. *Shadows and Spirits.* It must be . . .

He climbs up the bookcase, which is horrifying as it rises up at him. Grabbing at him with his every step.
He pulls the book from the shelf. It comes out and the noise and chaos suddenly stop.

Is that—

Suddenly there's a smashing and ALBUS *and* DELPHI *fall out of the shelves and down to the floor.*

We beat it. We beat the library.

ALBUS

Delphi, are you . . . ?

DELPHI

Wow. Quite a ride.

ALBUS *notices the book* SCORPIUS *is holding to his chest.*

ALBUS

Is that? Scorpius? What's inside that book?

DELPHI

I think we should find out don't you?

SCORPIUS *opens the book. In the centre of it – a spinning Time-Turner.*

SCORPIUS

We've found the Time-Turner – I never thought we'd get this far.

ALBUS

Mate, now we've got this, the next stop is saving Cedric. Our journey has only just begun.

SCORPIUS

Only just begun and it's almost half-killed us. Good. This is going to be good.

Whispers rise to a roar. And we cut to black.

INTERVAL

PART ONE

ACT TWO

ACT TWO   SCENE ONE

DREAM, PRIVET DRIVE, CUPBOARD UNDER THE STAIRS

AUNT PETUNIA
Harry. Harry. These pots aren't clean. THESE POTS ARE A DISGRACE. HARRY POTTER. Wake up.

YOUNG HARRY *wakes to see* AUNT PETUNIA *bearing down on him.*

YOUNG HARRY
Aunt Petunia. What time is it?

AUNT PETUNIA
Time enough. You know, when we agreed to take you in, we hoped we could improve you – build you – make you a decent human being. So I suppose it's only ourselves we've got to blame that you've turned out – such a limp disappointment.

YOUNG HARRY
I try—

AUNT PETUNIA
Trying is not succeeding, though, is it? There are grease smears on the glasses. There are scuff marks on the pots. Now get up and go to the kitchen and get scrubbing.

97

He gets out of bed. There's a wet smear down the back of his trousers.

Oh no. Oh no. What have you done? You've wet the bed, again.

She pulls back the covers.

This is very unacceptable.

YOUNG HARRY

I'm ... sorry, I think I was having a nightmare.

AUNT PETUNIA

You disgusting boy. Only animals wet themselves. Animals and disgusting little boys.

YOUNG HARRY

It was about my mum and dad. I think I saw them – I think I saw them – die?

AUNT PETUNIA

And why would I have the slightest bit of interest in that?

YOUNG HARRY

There was a man shouting Adkava Ad-something Acabra – Ad – and the noise of a snake hissing. I could hear my mum scream.

AUNT PETUNIA *takes a moment to reset herself.*

AUNT PETUNIA

If you were really reliving their death, all you'd hear would be a screech of brakes and a horrific thud. Your parents died in a car accident. You know that. I don't think your mother had even time to scream. Lord spare you the details more than that. Now strip those sheets, get in the kitchen and get scrubbing. I don't want to have to tell you again.

She exits with a bang.

And YOUNG HARRY *is left holding the sheets.*

And the stage contorts and trees rise as the dream twists into something else entirely.

Suddenly, ALBUS *appears and stands looking at* YOUNG HARRY.

And then right from the back of the room Parseltongue whispers around everyone.

He's coming. He's coming.

Words said with an unmistakeable voice. The voice of VOLDEMORT . . .

Haaarry Potttttter . . .

ACT TWO SCENE TWO

HARRY AND GINNY POTTER'S HOUSE, STAIRCASE

HARRY *wakes in the darkness, breathing deeply. His exhaustion palpable, his fear overwhelming.*

HARRY
Lumos.

    GINNY *enters, surprised by the light.*

GINNY
Okay ... ?

HARRY
I was sleeping.

GINNY
You were.

HARRY
You weren't. Any – news? Any owls or ... ?

GINNY
None.

HARRY
I was dreaming – I was under the stairs and then I – I heard him – Voldemort – so clearly.

GINNY
Voldemort?

HARRY

And then I saw – Albus. In red – he was wearing Durmstrang robes.

GINNY

Durmstrang robes?

HARRY *thinks.*

HARRY

Ginny, I think I know where he is . . .

ACT TWO   SCENE THREE

HOGWARTS, HEADMISTRESS'S OFFICE

HARRY *and* GINNY *stand in* PROFESSOR McGONAGALL's *office.*

PROFESSOR McGONAGALL
  And we don't know where in the Forbidden Forest?

HARRY
  I haven't had a dream like it for years. But Albus was there.
  I know he was.

GINNY
  We need to get searching as quickly as possible.

PROFESSOR McGONAGALL
  I can give you Professor Longbottom – his knowledge of
  plants might be useful – and—

  Suddenly there is a rumble in the chimney. PROFESSOR
  McGONAGALL *looks at it, concerned. Then* HERMIONE
  tumbles out.

HERMIONE
  Is it true? Can I help?

PROFESSOR McGONAGALL
  Minister – this is quite unexpected . . .

GINNY
  That may be my fault – I persuaded them to put out

an emergency edition of the *Daily Prophet*. Asking for
volunteers.

PROFESSOR McGONAGALL

Right. Very sensible. I expect ... there will be quite a few.

RON *bursts in. Covered in soot. Wearing a gravy-stained
dinner napkin.*

RON

Have I missed anything – I couldn't work out which Floo
to travel to. Ended up in the kitchen somehow. (HERMIONE
glares as he pulls the napkin off himself.) What?

*Suddenly there is another rumble in the chimney and
DRACO comes down hard, surrounded by cascading soot
and dust.*

*Everyone looks at him, surprised. He stands and brushes
the soot off himself.*

DRACO

Sorry about your floor, Minerva.

PROFESSOR McGONAGALL

I dare say it's my fault for owning a chimney.

HARRY

Quite a surprise to see you, Draco. I thought you didn't
believe in my dreams.

DRACO

I don't, but I do trust your luck. Harry Potter is always
where the action is at. And I need my son back with me
and safe.

GINNY

Then let's get to the Forbidden Forest and find them both.

ACT TWO   SCENE FOUR

EDGE OF THE FORBIDDEN FOREST

ALBUS *and* DELPHI *face each other, holding wands.*

ALBUS

Expelliarmus!

DELPHI's *wand flies through the air.*

DELPHI

You're getting it now. You're good at this.

She takes her wand back from him.
In a posh voice.

'You're a positively disarming young man.'

ALBUS

Expelliarmus!

Her wand flies back again.

DELPHI

And we have a winner.

The two high-five.

ALBUS

I've never been good at spells.

SCORPIUS *appears at the back of the stage. He looks at his friend talking to a girl – and part of him likes it and part of him doesn't.*

DELPHI

I was rubbish – and then something clicked. And it will for you too. Not that I'm a super witch or anything but I think you're becoming quite some wizard, Albus Potter.

ALBUS

Then you should stick around – teach me more—

DELPHI

Of course I'm sticking around, we're friends aren't we?

ALBUS

Yes. Yes. Definitely friends. Definitely.

DELPHI

Great. Wizzo!

SCORPIUS

What's wizzo?

SCORPIUS *steps forward decisively.*

ALBUS

Cracked the spell. I mean, it's pretty basic, but I was – well, I cracked it.

SCORPIUS (*over-enthusiastic, trying to join in*)

And I've found our way through to the school. Listen, are we sure this will work . . .

DELPHI

Yes!

ALBUS

It's a brilliant plan. The secret to not getting Cedric killed is to stop him winning the Triwizard Tournament. If he doesn't win, he can't be killed.

SCORPIUS

And I understand that but . . .

ALBUS

So we just need to mess up his chances supremely badly in task one. The first task is getting a golden egg from a dragon – how did Cedric distract the dragon—

> DELPHI *puts her hand in the air.* ALBUS *grins and points at her. These two are getting on really well now.*

Diggory.

DELPHI

—by transfiguring a stone into a dog.

ALBUS

—well, a little Expelliarmus and he won't be able to do that.

> SCORPIUS *isn't enjoying the* DELPHI-ALBUS *double act.*

SCORPIUS

Okay, two points, first point we're certain the dragon won't kill him?

DELPHI

It's always two points with him isn't it? Of course it won't. This is Hogwarts. They won't let damage happen to any of the champions.

SCORPIUS

Okay, second *point* – more significant *point* – we're going back without any knowledge of whether we can travel back afterwards. Which is exciting. Maybe we should just – try going back an hour, say, first and then . . .

DELPHI

I'm sorry, Scorpius, we've no time to waste. Waiting here this close to the school is just too dangerous – I'm sure they'll be looking for you and . . .

ALBUS

She's right.

DELPHI

Now, you're going to need to wear these—

She pulls out two large paper bags. The boys pull out robes from them.

ALBUS

But these are Durmstrang robes.

DELPHI

My uncle's idea. If you are in Hogwarts robes people will expect to know who you are. But there are two other schools competing at the Triwizard Tournament – and if you're in Durmstrang robes – well, you can fade into the background, can't you?

ALBUS

Good thinking! Hang on, where are your robes?

DELPHI

Albus, I'm flattered, but I don't think I can pretend to be a student, do you? I'll just keep in the background, and pretend to be a – ooh, maybe I could pretend to be a dragon tamer. You're doing all the spell stuff anyway.

SCORPIUS *looks at her and then at* ALBUS.

SCORPIUS

You shouldn't come.

DELPHI

What?

SCORPIUS

You're right. We don't need you for the spell. And if you can't wear student robes – you're too big a risk. Sorry, Delphi, you shouldn't come.

DELPHI

But I have to – he's my cousin. Albus?

ALBUS

I think he's right. I'm sorry.

DELPHI

What?

ALBUS

We won't mess up.

DELPHI

But without me – you won't be able to work the
Time-Turner.

SCORPIUS

You taught us how to use the Time-Turner.

> DELPHI *is really upset.*

DELPHI

No. I won't let you do this . . .

ALBUS

You told your uncle to trust us. Now it's your turn. The
school is close now. We should leave you here.

> DELPHI *looks at them both and takes a deep breath. She*
> *nods to herself and smiles.*

DELPHI

Then go. But – just know this . . . today you get an
opportunity few are given – today you get to change
history – to change time itself. But more than all that,
today you get the chance to give an old man his son back.

> *She smiles. She looks at* ALBUS. *She leans down and*
> *gently kisses him on both cheeks.*
> *She walks away into the woodland.* ALBUS *stares after her.*

SCORPIUS

She didn't kiss me – did you notice? (*He looks at his friend.*)
Are you okay, Albus? You look a little pale. And red. Pale
and red at the same time.

ALBUS

Let's do this.

ACT TWO SCENE FIVE

THE FORBIDDEN FOREST

*The forest seems to grow bigger, thicker, and amongst the trees –
people searching – looking for the missing wizards. But slowly people
melt away until* HARRY *is left alone.*

He hears something. He turns to his right.

HARRY
Albus? Scorpius? Albus?

> *And then he hears the sound of hooves.* HARRY *is startled.*
> *He looks around for where the noise is coming from.*
> *Suddenly* BANE *steps forward into the light. He is a*
> *magnificent centaur.*

BANE
Harry Potter.

HARRY
Good. You still recognise me, Bane.

BANE
You've grown older.

HARRY
I have.

BANE
But not wiser. For you trespass on our land.

HARRY

I have always respected the centaurs. We are not enemies.
You fought bravely at the Battle of Hogwarts. And I fought
beside you.

BANE

I did my part. But for my herd, and our honour. Not for you.
And after the battle, the forest was deemed centaur land.
And if you're on our land – without permission – then you
are our enemy.

HARRY

My son is missing, Bane. I need help finding him.

BANE

And he is here? In our forest?

HARRY

Yes.

BANE

Then he is as stupid as you are.

HARRY

Can you help me Bane?

> *There's a pause.* BANE *looks down at* HARRY *imperiously.*

BANE

I can only tell you what I know ... but I tell you not for
your benefit but for the benefit of my herd. The centaurs do
not need another war.

HARRY

Neither do we. What do you know?

BANE

I've seen your son, Harry Potter. Seen him in the
movements of the stars.

HARRY

You've seen him in the stars?

BANE

I can't tell you where he is. I can't tell you how you'll find him.

HARRY

But you've seen something? You've divined something?

BANE

There is a black cloud around your son, a dangerous black cloud.

HARRY

Around Albus?

BANE

A black cloud that may endanger us all. You'll find your son again, Harry Potter. But then you could lose him forever.

He makes a sound like a horse's cry – and then makes hard away – leaving a bewildered HARRY *behind.*

HARRY *begins to search again – now with even more fervour.*

HARRY

Albus! Albus!

ACT TWO   SCENE SIX

EDGE OF THE FORBIDDEN FOREST

SCORPIUS *and* ALBUS *round a corner to be faced with a gap in the trees . . .*

A gap through which is visible . . . a glorious light . . .

SCORPIUS

And there it is . . .

ALBUS

Hogwarts. Never seen this view of it before.

SCORPIUS

Still get a tingle, don't you? When you see it?

And revealed through the trees is HOGWARTS – a splendid mass of bulbous buildings and towers.

From the moment I first heard of it, I was desperate to go. I mean, Dad didn't much like it there but even the way he described it . . . From the age of ten I'd check the *Daily Prophet* first thing every morning – certain some sort of tragedy would have befallen it – certain I wouldn't get to go.

ALBUS

And then you got there and it turned out to be terrible after all.

SCORPIUS
Not for me.

ALBUS looks at his friend, shocked.

All I ever wanted to do was go to Hogwarts and have a
mate to get up to mayhem with. Just like Harry Potter. And
I got his son. How crazily fortunate is that.

ALBUS
But I'm nothing like my dad.

SCORPIUS
You're better. You're my best friend, Albus. And this is
mayhem to the nth degree. Which is great, thumbs-up
great, it's just – I have got to say – I don't mind admitting –
I am a tiny bit – just a tiny bit scared.

ALBUS looks at SCORPIUS and smiles.

ALBUS
You're my best friend too. And don't worry – I have a good
feeling about this.

*We hear RON's voice from off – he's clearly in close
proximity.*

RON
Albus? Albus!

ALBUS turns towards it, scared.

ALBUS
But we've got to go – now.

*ALBUS takes the Time-Turner from SCORPIUS – he presses
down upon it and the Time-Turner begins to vibrate, and
then explodes into a storm of movement.*
*And with it the stage starts to transform. The two boys
look at it.*

And there is a giant whoosh of light. A smash of noise. And time stops. And then it turns over, thinks a bit, and begins spooling backwards, slow at first . . .

And then it speeds up.

ACT TWO SCENE SEVEN

TRIWIZARD TOURNAMENT, EDGE OF
THE FORBIDDEN FOREST, 1994

Suddenly everything is a riot of noise as a crowd consumes ALBUS *and* SCORPIUS.

And suddenly 'the greatest showman on earth' (his words, not ours) is on stage, using Sonorus to amplify his voice, and . . . well . . . he's having a ball.

LUDO BAGMAN
Ladies and gentlemen, boys and girls, I give you –
the greatest – the fabulous – the one – and the only
TRIWIZARD TOURNAMENT.

> *There's a loud cheer.*

If you're from Hogwarts. Give me a cheer.

> *There's a loud cheer.*

If you're from Durmstrang – give me a cheer.

> *There's a loud cheer.*

AND IF YOU'RE FROM BEAUXBATONS GIVE ME A
CHEER.

> *There's a slightly limp cheer.*

Slightly less enthusiastic from the French there.

SCORPIUS *(smiling)*
This has worked. That's Ludo Bagman.

LUDO BAGMAN
And there they are. Ladies and gentlemen – boys and girls –
I present to you – the reason why we're all here – THE
CHAMPIONS. Representing Durmstrang, what eyebrows,
what a gait, what a boy, there's nothing he won't try on a
broomstick, it's Viktor Krazy Krum.

SCORPIUS and ALBUS *(who are really getting into playing the
Durmstrang students now)*
Go go Krazy Krum. Go go Krazy Krum.

LUDO BAGMAN
From the Beauxbatons Academy – zut alors, it's Fleur
Delacour!

There's some polite applause.

And from Hogwarts not one but two students, he makes us
all go weaky at the kneesy, he's Cedric Delicious Diggory.

The crowd go wild.

And then the other – you know him as the Boy Who
Lived, I know him as the boy who keeps surprising us all . . .

ALBUS
That's my dad.

LUDO BAGMAN
Yes, it's Harry Plucky Potter.

*There's cheering. Particularly from a nervous-looking
girl at the edge of the crowd – this is YOUNG HERMIONE
(played by the same actress as plays ROSE). It is noticeable
that the cheering for Harry is slightly less than that for
Cedric.*

And now – silence please all. The – first – task. Retrieving a golden egg. From a nest of – ladies and gentlemen, boys and girls, I give you – DRAGONS. And guiding the dragons – CHARLIE WEASLEY.

There are more cheers.

YOUNG HERMIONE
If you're going to stand so close I'd rather you didn't breathe on me quite so much.

SCORPIUS
Rose? What are you doing here?

YOUNG HERMIONE
Who's Rose? And what's happened to your accent?

ALBUS (*with a bad accent*)
Sorry. Hermione. He's got you mixed up with someone else.

YOUNG HERMIONE
How do you know my name?

LUDO BAGMAN
And with no time to lose, let's bring out our first champion – facing a Swedish Short-Snout, I give you – CEDRIC DIGGORY!

A dragon roar distracts YOUNG HERMIONE, *and* ALBUS *readies his wand.*

And Cedric Diggory has entered the stage. And he seems ready. Scared but ready. He dodges this way. He dodges that. The girls swoon as he dives for cover. They cry as one: don't damage our Diggory, Mr Dragon.

SCORPIUS *looks concerned.*

SCORPIUS
Albus, something is going wrong. The Time-Turner, it's shaking.

> *A ticking begins, an incessant, dangerous, ticking. It's coming from the Time-Turner.*

LUDO BAGMAN
    And Cedric skirts left and he dives right – and he readies his wand – what has this young, brave, handsome man got up his sleevies now—

ALBUS *(extending his wand)*
    Expelliarmus!

> CEDRIC's *wand is summoned to* ALBUS's *hand.*

LUDO BAGMAN
    —but no, what's this? Is it Dark Magic or is it something else entirely – Cedric Diggory is disarmed—

SCORPIUS
    Albus, I think the Time-Turner – something is wrong . . .

> *The Time-Turner's ticking gets louder still.*

LUDO BAGMAN
    It's all going wrong for Diggors. This could be the end of the task for him. The end of the tournament.

> SCORPIUS *grabs* ALBUS.
> *There's a crescendo in the ticking and a flash.*
> *And time is turned back to the present, with* ALBUS *hollering in pain.*

SCORPIUS
    Albus! Did it hurt you? Albus are you—

ALBUS
    What happened?

SCORPIUS
    There must be some limit – the Time-Turner must have some kind of *time* limit . . .

ALBUS

Do you think we've done it? Do you think we've changed anything?

> *Suddenly the stage is invaded from all sides by* HARRY, RON *(who now has a side parting and whose wardrobe choices have become rather more staid)*, GINNY *and* DRACO. SCORPIUS *looks at them all – and slips the Time-Turner back into his pocket.* ALBUS *looks at them rather more blankly – he's in a lot of pain.*

RON

I told you. I told you I saw them.

SCORPIUS

I think we're about to find out.

ALBUS

Hello, Dad. Is something wrong?

> HARRY *looks at his son disbelievingly.*

HARRY

Yes. You could say that.

> ALBUS *collapses on to the floor.* HARRY *and* GINNY *rush to help.*

ACT TWO   SCENE EIGHT

HOGWARTS, HOSPITAL WING

ALBUS *is asleep in a hospital bed.* HARRY *sits, troubled, beside him. Above them is a picture of a concerned, kindly man.* HARRY *rubs his eyes, stands and walks around the room, stretching his back.*

And then he meets eyes with the painting. Which looks startled to be spotted. And HARRY *looks startled back.*

HARRY

Professor Dumbledore.

DUMBLEDORE

Good evening, Harry.

HARRY

I've missed you. Whenever I've dropped in on the Headmistress lately, your frame's been empty.

DUMBLEDORE

Ah, well, I do like to pop into my other portraits now and then. (*He looks at* ALBUS.) Will he be all right?

HARRY

He's been out twenty-four hours, mostly in order so Madam Pomfrey could reset his arm. She said it was the strangest thing . . . it's like it was broken twenty years ago and allowed to set in the 'most contrary' of directions. She says he'll be fine.

DUMBLEDORE

A difficult thing, I imagine, to watch your child in pain.

HARRY *looks up at* DUMBLEDORE, *and then down at* ALBUS.

HARRY

I've never asked how you felt about me naming him after you, have I?

DUMBLEDORE

Candidly, Harry, it seemed a great weight to place upon the poor boy.

HARRY

I need your help. I need your advice. Bane says Albus is in danger. How do I protect my son, Dumbledore?

DUMBLEDORE

You ask me, of all people, how to protect a boy in terrible danger? We cannot protect the young from harm. Pain must and will come.

HARRY

So I'm supposed to stand and watch?

DUMBLEDORE

No. You're supposed to teach him how to meet life.

HARRY

How? He won't listen.

DUMBLEDORE

Perhaps he's waiting for you to see him clearly.

HARRY *frowns as he tries to digest this.*

(*With sensitivity.*) It is a portrait's curse and blessing to . . . hear things. At the school, at the Ministry, I hear people talking . . .

HARRY

And what is the gossip about me and my son?

DUMBLEDORE

Not gossip. Concern. That you two are struggling. That

he's difficult. That he is angry with you. I have formed the impression that – perhaps – you are blinded by your love for him.

HARRY
Blinded?

DUMBLEDORE
You must see him as he is, Harry. You must look for what's wounding him.

HARRY
Haven't I seen him as he is? What's wounding my son? (*He thinks.*) Or is it who's wounding my son?

ALBUS (*mumbles in his sleep*)
Dad . . .

HARRY
This black cloud, it's someone isn't it? Not something?

DUMBLEDORE
Ah really, what does my opinion matter any more? I am paint and memory, Harry, paint and memory. And I never had a son.

HARRY
But I need your advice.

ALBUS
Dad?

> HARRY *looks at* ALBUS *and then back at* DUMBLEDORE. *But* DUMBLEDORE *is gone.*

HARRY
No, where have you gone now?

ALBUS
We're in – the hospital wing?

> HARRY *turns his attention back to* ALBUS.

HARRY (*discombobulated*)
Yes. And you're – you will be fine. For recuperation, Madam

Pomfrey wasn't sure what to prescribe and said you should probably eat lots of – chocolate. Actually, do you mind if I have some? I've got something to tell you and I don't think you'll like it.

> ALBUS *looks at his dad, what does he have to say? He decides not to engage.*

ALBUS
Okay. I think.

> HARRY *takes some chocolate. He eats a big chunk.* ALBUS *looks at his dad, confused.*

Better?

HARRY
Much.

> *He holds out the chocolate to his son.* ALBUS *takes a piece. Father and son munch together.*

The arm, how does it feel?

> ALBUS *flexes his arm.*

ALBUS
It feels great.

HARRY (*soft*)
Where did you go Albus? I can't tell you what it did to us – your mum was worried sick . . .

> ALBUS *looks up, he is a great liar.*

ALBUS
We decided we didn't want to come to school. We thought we could start again – in the Muggle world – we discovered we were wrong. We were coming back to Hogwarts when you found us.

HARRY

> In Durmstrang robes?

ALBUS

> The robes were ... the whole thing – Scorpius and I – we didn't think.

HARRY

> And why ... why did you run? Because of me? Because of what I said?

ALBUS

> I don't know. Hogwarts isn't actually that pleasant a place when you don't fit in.

HARRY

> And did Scorpius – encourage you to – go?

ALBUS

> Scorpius? No.

> > HARRY *looks at* ALBUS, *trying to see almost an aura around him, thinking deeply.*

HARRY

> I need you to stay away from Scorpius Malfoy.

ALBUS

> What? Scorpius?

HARRY

> I don't know how you became friends in the first place, but you did – and now – I need you to—

ALBUS

> My best friend? My only friend?

HARRY

> He's dangerous.

ALBUS

> Scorpius? Dangerous? Have you met him? Dad, if you honestly think he's the son of Voldemort—

HARRY

I don't know what he is, I just know you need to stay away
from him. Bane told me—

ALBUS

Who's Bane?

HARRY

A centaur with profound divination skills. He said there's a
black cloud around you and—

ALBUS

A black cloud?

HARRY

And I have very good reason to believe that Dark Magic
is in a resurgence and I need to keep you safe from it. Safe
from him. Safe from Scorpius.

ALBUS *hesitates a moment, and then his face strengthens.*

ALBUS

And if I won't? Stay away from him?

HARRY *looks at his son, thinking quickly.*

HARRY

There's a map. It used to be used for those wanting to
get up to no good. Now we're going to use it to keep an
eye – a permanent eye – on you. Professor McGonagall
will watch your every movement. Any time you are seen
together – she'll come flying – any time you attempt to leave
Hogwarts – she'll fly. I expect you to go to your lessons, none
of which you will now share with Scorpius, and between
times, you will stay in the Gryffindor common room!

ALBUS

You can't make me go into Gryffindor! I'm Slytherin!

HARRY

Don't play games Albus, you know what house you are.
If she finds you with Scorpius – I will fix you with a

spell – which will allow me eyes and ears into your every movement, your every conversation. In the meantime, investigations will begin in my department as to his true heritage.

ALBUS (*starting to cry*)
But Dad – you can't – that's just not . . .

HARRY
I thought for a long time I wasn't a good enough dad for you because you didn't like me. It's only now I realise that I don't need you to like me, I need you to obey me because I'm your dad and I do know better. I'm sorry, Albus. It has to be this way.

ACT TWO   SCENE NINE

HOGWARTS, STAIRCASES

ALBUS *pursues* HARRY *across the stage.*

ALBUS
What if I run? I'll run.

HARRY
Albus, get back in bed.

ALBUS
I'll run away again.

HARRY
No. You won't.

ALBUS
I will – and this time I'll make sure Ron can't find us.

RON
Do I hear my name?

> RON *enters on a staircase, his side parting now super-aggressive, his robes just a little bit too short, his clothes now spectacularly staid.*

ALBUS
Uncle Ron! Thank Dumbledore. If ever we needed one of your jokes it's now . . .

RON *frowns, confused.*

RON

Jokes? I don't know any jokes.

ALBUS

Of course you do. You run a joke shop.

RON *(now supremely confused)*

A joke shop? Well now. Anyway I'm pleased I caught you . . . I was going to bring some sweets – for a, uh, sort of, a, get well soon, but, uh . . . actually Padma – she thinks about things a lot more – deeply than I do – and she thought it'd be nicer for you to get something useful for school. So we got you a – set of quills. Yes. Yes. Yes. Look at these bad boys. Top of the range.

ALBUS

Who's Padma?

HARRY *frowns at* ALBUS.

HARRY

Your aunt.

ALBUS

I have an Aunt Padma?

RON

(To HARRY*)* Taken a Confundus Charm to the head, has he? *(To* ALBUS*)* My wife, Padma. You remember. Talks slightly too close to your face, smells a bit minty. *(Leans in.)* Padma, mother of Panju! *(To* HARRY.*)* That's why I'm here, of course. Panju. He's in trouble again. I wanted to just send a Howler but Padma insisted I come in person. I don't know why. He just laughs at me.

ALBUS

But . . . you're married to Hermione.

Beat. RON *doesn't understand this at all.*

RON

Hermione? No. Nooooo. Merlin's beard.

HARRY

Albus has also forgotten that he was sorted into Gryffindor.
Conveniently.

RON

Yes, well, sorry, old chap, but you're a Gryffindor.

ALBUS

But how did I get sorted into Gryffindor?

RON

You persuaded the Sorting Hat, don't you remember? Panju
bet you that you couldn't get into Gryffindor if your life
depended on it, so you chose Gryffindor to spite him. I can't
blame you, (dryly) we'd all like to wipe the smile off his face
sometimes wouldn't we? (Terrified.) Please don't tell Padma
I said that.

ALBUS

Who's Panju?

> RON and HARRY stare at ALBUS.

RON

Bloody hell, you're really not yourself are you? Anyway,
better go, before I'm sent a Howler myself.

> He stumbles on, not even an inch of the man he was.

ALBUS

But that doesn't ... make sense.

HARRY

Albus, whatever you're feigning, it isn't working, I will not
change my mind.

ALBUS

Dad, you have two choices, either you take me to—

HARRY

No, you're the one with the choice Albus. You do this,

or you get in deeper – much deeper – trouble, do you
understand?

SCORPIUS

Albus? You're okay. That's fantastic.

HARRY

He's completely cured. And we've got to go.

ALBUS *looks up at* SCORPIUS *and his heart breaks. He
walks on.*

SCORPIUS

Are you mad at me? What's going on?

ALBUS *stops and turns to* SCORPIUS.

ALBUS

Did it work? Did any of it work?

SCORPIUS

No ... but, Albus—

HARRY

Albus. Whatever gibberish you're talking, you need to stop
it, now. This is your final warning.

ALBUS *looks torn between his dad and his friend.*

ALBUS

I can't, okay?

SCORPIUS

You can't what?

ALBUS

Just – we'll be better off without each other, okay?

SCORPIUS *is left looking up after him. Heartbroken.*

ACT TWO SCENE TEN

HOGWARTS, HEADMISTRESS'S OFFICE

PROFESSOR McGONAGALL *is full of unhappiness,* HARRY *is full of purpose,* GINNY *is not sure what she's supposed to be.*

PROFESSOR McGONAGALL

I'm not sure this is what the Marauder's Map was intended for.

HARRY

If you see them together, then get to them as quickly as possible, and keep them separate.

PROFESSOR McGONAGALL

Harry, are you sure this is the right decision? Because far be it from me to doubt the wisdom of the centaurs but Bane is an extremely angry centaur and . . . it's not beyond him to twist the constellations for his own ends.

HARRY

I trust Bane. Albus is to stay away from Scorpius. For his sake, and others'.

GINNY

I think what Harry means is . . .

HARRY *(with finality)*

The Professor knows what I mean.

GINNY *looks at* HARRY, *surprised that he'd talk to her that way.*

PROFESSOR McGONAGALL
Albus has been checked by the greatest witches and wizards in the country and no one can find or sense a hex or a curse.

HARRY
And Dumbledore – Dumbledore said—

PROFESSOR McGONAGALL
What?

HARRY
His portrait. We spoke. He said some things which made sense—

PROFESSOR McGONAGALL
Dumbledore is dead, Harry. And I've told you before, portraits don't represent even half of their subjects.

HARRY
He said love had blinded me.

PROFESSOR McGONAGALL
A headteacher's portrait is a memoir. It is supposed to be a support mechanism for the decisions I have to make. But I was advised as I took this job to not mistake the painting for the person. And you would be well-advised to do the same.

HARRY
But he was right. I see it now.

PROFESSOR McGONAGALL
Harry, you've been put under enormous pressure, the loss of Albus, the search for him, the fears as to what your scar might mean. But trust me when I tell you, you are making a mistake—

HARRY
Albus didn't like me before. He might not like me again.

But he will be safe. With the greatest respect, Minerva –
you don't have children—

GINNY
Harry!

HARRY
—you don't understand.

PROFESSOR McGONAGALL (*deeply hurt*)
I'd hope that a lifetime spent in the teaching profession
would mean—

HARRY
This map will reveal to you where my son is at all times – I
expect you to use it. And if I hear you don't – then I will
come down on this school as hard as I can – using the full
force of the Ministry – is that understood?

PROFESSOR McGONAGALL (*bewildered by this vitriol*)
Perfectly.

GINNY *looks at* HARRY, *unsure of what he's become. He
doesn't look back.*

ACT TWO   SCENE ELEVEN

HOGWARTS, DEFENCE AGAINST THE DARK ARTS CLASS

ALBUS *enters the classroom, slightly unsure.*

HERMIONE

Ah yes. Our train absconder. Finally joining us.

ALBUS

Hermione?

He looks amazed. HERMIONE *is standing at the front of the lesson.*

HERMIONE

Professor Granger I believe is my name, Potter.

ALBUS

What are you doing here?

HERMIONE

Teaching. For my sins. What are you doing here? Learning I hope.

ALBUS

But you're ... you're ... Minister for Magic.

HERMIONE

Been having those dreams again have you Potter? Today we're going to look at Patronus Charms.

ALBUS *(amazed)*
> You're our Defence Against the Dark Arts teacher?

There are titters.

HERMIONE
> Losing patience now. Ten points from Gryffindor for
> stupidity.

POLLY CHAPMAN *(standing, full of affront)*
> No. No. He's doing it deliberately. He hates Gryffindor and
> everyone knows it.

HERMIONE
> Sit down Polly Chapman before this gets even worse. (POLLY
> *sighs and then sits.)* And I suggest you join her, Albus. And
> end this charade.

ALBUS
> But you're not this mean.

HERMIONE
> And that's twenty points from Gryffindor to assure Albus
> Potter that I am this mean.

YANN FREDERICKS
> If you don't sit down right now, Albus . . .

> ALBUS *sits.*

ALBUS
> Can I just say—

HERMIONE
> No, you can't. Just keep quiet Potter, otherwise you'll lose
> what limited popularity you already have. Now who can tell
> me what a Patronus is? No? No one. You really are a most
> disappointing bunch.

> HERMIONE *smiles a thin smile. She really is quite mean.*

ALBUS

No. This is stupid. Where's Rose? She'll tell you that you're being ridiculous.

HERMIONE

Who's Rose? Your invisible friend?

ALBUS

Rose Granger-Weasley! Your daughter! *(He realises.)* Of course . . . because you and Ron aren't married Rose—

There's giggling.

HERMIONE

How dare you! Fifty points from Gryffindor. And I assure you if anyone interrupts me again it'll be a hundred points . . .

She stares around the room. No one moves a muscle.

Good. A Patronus is a magical charm, a projection of all your most positive feelings and takes the shape of the animal with whom you share the deepest affinity. It is a gift of light. If you can conjure a Patronus, you can protect yourself against the world. Which, in some of our cases, seems like a necessity sooner rather than later.

ACT TWO SCENE TWELVE

HOGWARTS, STAIRCASES

ALBUS *walks up a staircase. Looking around as he does.*

He doesn't see anything. He exits. The staircases move in almost a dance.

SCORPIUS *enters behind him. He thinks he's seen* ALBUS, *he realises he isn't there.*

He slumps down to the floor as the staircase sweeps around.

MADAM HOOCH *enters and walks up the staircase. At the top, she gestures for* SCORPIUS *to move.*

He does. And slopes off – his abject loneliness clear.

ALBUS *enters and walks up one staircase.*

SCORPIUS *enters and walks up another.*

The staircases meet. The two boys look at each other.

Lost and hopeful – all at once.

And then ALBUS *looks away and the moment is broken – and with it, possibly, the friendship.*

And now the staircases part – the two look at each other – one full of guilt – the other full of pain – both full of unhappiness.

ACT TWO   SCENE THIRTEEN

HARRY AND GINNY POTTER'S HOUSE, KITCHEN

GINNY *and* HARRY *watch each other warily. There is an argument due, and both of them know it.*

HARRY
This is the right decision.

GINNY
You almost sound convinced.

HARRY
You told me to be honest with him, but actually I needed to be honest with myself, trust what my heart was telling me . . .

GINNY
Harry, you have one of the greatest hearts of any wizard who ever lived, and I do not believe your heart told you to do this.

They hear a knock on the door.

Saved by the door.

She exits.

After a moment, DRACO *enters, consumed by anger but hiding it well.*

138

DRACO
I can't stay long. I won't need long.

HARRY
How can I help?

DRACO
I'm not here to antagonise you. But my son is in tears and I am his father and so I am here to ask why you would keep apart two good friends.

HARRY
I'm not keeping them apart.

DRACO
You've changed school timetables, you've threatened both teachers and Albus himself. Why?

HARRY *looks at* DRACO *carefully and then turns away.*

HARRY
I have to protect my son.

DRACO
From Scorpius?

HARRY
Bane told me he sensed a darkness around my son. Near my son.

DRACO
What are you implying, Potter?

HARRY *turns and looks* DRACO *dead in the eye.*

HARRY
Are you sure ... are you really sure he's yours Draco?

There's a deadly silence.

DRACO
You take that back ... right now.

But HARRY *doesn't take it back. So* DRACO *takes his wand out.*

139

HARRY
You do not want to do this.

DRACO
Yes I do.

HARRY
I don't want to hurt you, Draco.

DRACO
How interesting, because I do want to hurt you.

The two square up. And then release their wands.

DRACO *and* **HARRY**
Expelliarmus!

Their wands repel and then break apart.

DRACO
Incarcerous!

HARRY dodges a blast from DRACO's wand.

HARRY
Tarantallegra!

DRACO throws himself out of the way.

HARRY
You've been practising, Draco.

DRACO
And you've got sloppy, Potter. Densaugeo!

HARRY just manages to get out of the way.

HARRY
Rictusempra!

DRACO uses a chair to block the blast.

DRACO
Flipendo!

HARRY is sent twirling through the air. DRACO laughs.

Keep up, old man.

HARRY
We're the same age, Draco.

DRACO
I wear it better.

HARRY
Brachiabindo!

DRACO is bound tightly.

DRACO
That really the best you got? Emancipare!

DRACO releases his own binds.

Levicorpus!

HARRY has to throw himself out of the way.

Mobilicorpus! Oh, this is too much fun . . .

DRACO bounces HARRY up and down on the table. And then as HARRY rolls away, DRACO jumps on to the table – he readies his wand, but as he does HARRY hits him with a spell . . .

HARRY
Obscuro!

DRACO releases himself from his blindfold as soon as it hits.

The two square up – HARRY throws a chair.
DRACO ducks underneath it and slows the chair with his wand.

GINNY
I only left this room three minutes ago!

She looks at the mess of the kitchen. She looks at the chairs suspended in the air. She signals them back to the floor with her wand.

(Drier than dry.) What did I miss?

ACT TWO SCENE FOURTEEN

HOGWARTS, STAIRCASES

SCORPIUS *walks unhappily down a staircase.*
DELPHI *scurries in from the other side.*

DELPHI

So – technically – I shouldn't be here.

SCORPIUS

Delphi?

DELPHI

In fact, technically I'm endangering our entire operation ...
which is not ... well, I'm not a natural risk-taker as you
know. I've never been to Hogwarts. Pretty lax security here
isn't there? And so many portraits. And corridors. And
ghosts! This half-headless strange-looking ghost told me
where I could find you, can you believe that?

SCORPIUS

You've never been to Hogwarts?

DELPHI

I was – unwell – as a child – for a few years. Other people
got to go – I did not.

SCORPIUS

You were too – ill? I'm sorry, I didn't know that.

DELPHI

I don't advertise the fact – I prefer not to be seen as a tragic case, you know?

This registers with SCORPIUS. *He looks up to say something but* DELPHI *suddenly ducks from view as a student walks past.* SCORPIUS *tries to look casual until the student passes.*

Have they gone?

SCORPIUS

Delphi, maybe it is too dangerous for you to be here—

DELPHI

Well – someone's got to do something about this.

SCORPIUS

Delphi, none of it worked, time-turning, we failed.

DELPHI

I know. Albus owled me. The history books changed but not enough – Cedric still died. In fact, failing the first task only made him more determined to win the second.

SCORPIUS

And Ron and Hermione have gone completely skewwhiff – and I still haven't figured out why.

DELPHI

And that's why Cedric has to wait. It's all become quite confused and you're entirely right to be keeping hold of the Time-Turner, Scorpius. But what I meant was – someone's got to do something about the two of you.

SCORPIUS

Oh.

DELPHI

You're best friends. Every owl he sends I can feel your absence. He's destroyed by it.

SCORPIUS

Sounds like he's found a shoulder to cry on. How many owls has he sent you now?

DELPHI *smiles softly.*

Sorry. That's – I didn't mean – I just – don't understand what's going on. I've tried to see him, talk to him, but every time I do he runs off.

DELPHI

You know, I didn't have a best friend when I was your age. I wanted one. Desperately. When I was younger I even invented one but—

SCORPIUS

I had one of those too. Called Flurry. We fell out over the correct rules of Gobstones.

DELPHI

Albus needs you, Scorpius. That's a wonderful thing.

SCORPIUS

He needs me to do what?

DELPHI

That's the thing isn't it? About friendships. You don't know what he needs. You only know he needs it. Find him Scorpius. You two – you belong together.

ACT TWO SCENE FIFTEEN

HARRY AND GINNY POTTER'S HOUSE, KITCHEN

HARRY *and* DRACO *sit far apart.* GINNY *stands between them.*

DRACO
  Sorry about your kitchen, Ginny.

GINNY
  Oh, it's not my kitchen. Harry does most of the cooking.

DRACO
  I can't talk to him either. Scorpius. Especially since –
  Astoria has gone. I can't even talk about how losing her has
  affected him. As hard as I try, I can't reach him. You can't
  talk to Albus. I can't talk to Scorpius. That's what this is
  about. Not about my son being evil. Because as much as
  you might take the word of a haughty centaur, you know
  the power of friendship.

HARRY
  Draco, whatever you may think—

DRACO
  I always envied you them you know – Weasley and Granger.
  I had—

GINNY
  Crabbe and Goyle.

DRACO

Two lunks who wouldn't know one end of a broomstick
from another. You – the three of you – you shone you know?
You liked each other. You had fun. I envied you those
friendships more than anything else.

GINNY

I envied them too.

> HARRY *looks at* GINNY, *surprised.*

HARRY

I need to protect him—

DRACO

My father thought he was protecting me. Most of the time.
I think you have to make a choice – at a certain point – of
the man you want to be. And I tell you that at that time
you need a parent or a friend. And if you've learnt to hate
your parent by then and you have no friends . . . then you're
all alone. And being alone – that's so hard. I was alone.
And it sent me to a truly dark place. For a long time. Tom
Riddle was also a lonely child. You may not understand that
Harry, but I do – and I think Ginny does too.

GINNY

He's right.

DRACO

Tom Riddle didn't emerge from his dark place. And so Tom
Riddle became Lord Voldemort. Maybe the black cloud
Bane saw was Albus's loneliness. His pain. His hatred.
Don't lose the boy. You'll regret it. And so will he. Because
he needs you, and Scorpius, whether or not he now
knows it.

> HARRY *looks at* DRACO, *he thinks.*
> *He opens his mouth to speak. He thinks.*

GINNY
Harry. Will you get the Floo powder or shall I?

HARRY *looks up at his wife.*

———

ACT TWO   SCENE SIXTEEN

HOGWARTS, LIBRARY

SCORPIUS *arrives in the library. He looks left and right. And then he sees* ALBUS. *And* ALBUS *sees him.*

SCORPIUS
> Hi.

ALBUS
> Scorpius. I can't ...

SCORPIUS
> I know. You're in Gryffindor now. You don't want to see me now. But here I am anyway. Talking to you.

ALBUS
> Well, I can't talk, so—

SCORPIUS
> You have to. You think you can just ignore everything that's happened? The world has gone crazy, have you noticed?

ALBUS
> I know, okay? Ron's gone strange. Hermione's a professor, it's all wrong but—

SCORPIUS
> And Rose doesn't exist.

ALBUS

I know. Look, I don't understand everything, but you can't be here.

SCORPIUS

Because of what we did, Rose wasn't even born. Do you remember being told about the Triwizard Tournament Yule Ball? All the four Triwizard champions took a partner. Your dad took Parvati Patil, Viktor Krum took—

ALBUS

Hermione. And Ron got jealous and behaved like a prat.

SCORPIUS

Only he didn't. I found Rita Skeeter's book about them. And it's very different. Ron took Hermione to the ball.

ALBUS

What?

POLLY CHAPMAN

Ssshhh!

SCORPIUS *looks at* POLLY *and drops his volume.*

SCORPIUS

As friends. And they danced in a friendly way, and it was nice, and then he danced with Padma Patil and that was nicer, and they started dating and he changed a bit and then they got married and meanwhile Hermione became a—

ALBUS

—psychopath.

SCORPIUS

Hermione was supposed to go to that ball with Krum – do you know why she didn't? Because she had suspicions the two strange Durmstrang boys she met before the first task were somehow involved in the disappearance of Cedric's wand. She believed we, under Viktor's orders, cost Cedric the first task . . .

ALBUS

Wow.

SCORPIUS

And without Krum, Ron never got jealous and that jealousy
was all-important and so Ron and Hermione stayed very
good friends but never fell in love – never got married –
never had Rose.

ALBUS

So that's why Dad's so – did he change too?

SCORPIUS

I'm pretty sure your dad is exactly the same. Head of
Magical Law Enforcement. Married to Ginny. Three kids.

ALBUS

So why is he being such a—

A LIBRARIAN *enters at the back of the room.*

SCORPIUS

Have you heard me, Albus? This is bigger than you and
your dad. Professor Croaker's law – the furthest someone
can go back in time without the possibility of serious harm
to the traveller or time itself is five hours. And we went
back years. The smallest moment, the smallest change, it
creates ripples. And we – we've created really bad ripples.
Rose was never born because of what we did. Rose.

LIBRARIAN

Ssshhh!

ALBUS *thinks quickly.*

ALBUS

Fine, let's go back – fix it. Get Cedric and Rose back.

SCORPIUS

. . . is the wrong answer.

ALBUS

You've still got the Time-Turner, right? No one found it?

SCORPIUS *takes it out of his pocket.*

SCORPIUS
Yes, but ...

ALBUS *snatches it from his hand.*

No. Don't ... Albus. Don't you understand how bad things could get?

SCORPIUS *grabs for the Time-Turner,* ALBUS *pushes him back, they wrestle inexpertly.*

ALBUS
Things need fixing, Scorpius. Cedric still needs saving. Rose needs bringing back. We'll be more careful. Whatever Croaker says, trust me, trust us. We'll get it right this time.

SCORPIUS
No. We won't. Give it back, Albus! Give it back!

ALBUS
I can't. This is too important.

SCORPIUS
Yes it's too important – for us. We're not good at this stuff. We'll get it wrong.

ALBUS
Who's saying that we'll get it wrong?

SCORPIUS
I say. Because that's *what we do.* We mess things up. We lose. We're losers, true and total losers. Haven't you realised that yet?

ALBUS *finally gets the upper hand and pins* SCORPIUS *to the ground.*

ALBUS
Well, I wasn't a loser before I met you.

SCORPIUS

Albus, whatever you've got to prove to your dad – this isn't the way—

ALBUS

I don't have anything to prove to my dad. I've got to save Cedric to save Rose. And maybe, without you holding me back, I can make a proper go of it.

SCORPIUS

Without me? Oh poor Albus Potter. With his chip on his shoulder. Poor Albus Potter. So sad.

ALBUS

What are you saying?

SCORPIUS (*exploding*)

Try my life! People look at you because your dad's the famous Harry Potter, saviour of the wizarding world. People look at me because they think my dad is Voldemort. Voldemort.

ALBUS

Don't even—

SCORPIUS

Can you even slightly imagine what that's like? Have you even ever tried? No. Because you can't see beyond the end of your nose. Because you can't see beyond the end of your stupid thing with your dad. He will always be Harry Potter, you know that right? And you will always be his son. And I know it's hard, and the other kids are awful but you have to learn to be okay with that, because – there are worse things, okay?

Beat.

There was a moment I was excited, when I realised time was different, a moment when I thought maybe my mum hadn't got sick. Maybe my mum wasn't dead. But no, turns out, she was. I'm still the child of Voldemort, without a mother, giving sympathy to the boy who doesn't ever give anything back. So I'm sorry if I've ruined your life because I tell you – you wouldn't have a chance of ruining mine – it was already ruined. You just didn't make it better. Because you're a terrible – the most terrible – friend.

ALBUS digests this. He sees what he's done to his friend.

PROFESSOR McGONAGALL *(from off)*
Albus? Albus Potter. Scorpius Malfoy. Are you in there – together? Because I advise you not to be.

ALBUS looks at SCORPIUS, he pulls a cloak from his bag.

ALBUS
Quick. We need to hide.

SCORPIUS
What?

ALBUS
Scorpius, look at me.

SCORPIUS
That's the Invisibility Cloak? Isn't it James's?

ALBUS
If she finds us, we'll be forced apart forever. Please. I didn't understand. Please.

PROFESSOR McGONAGALL *(from off, trying to give them every chance)*
I am about to enter.

PROFESSOR McGONAGALL comes into the room, the Marauder's Map in her hands. The boys disappear beneath the cloak. She looks around exasperated.

Well, where have they – I never wanted this thing and now it's playing tricks on me.

She thinks. She looks back at the map. She identifies where they should be. She looks around the room.

Objects move as the boys invisibly move past them. She sees where they're heading, she makes to block them. But they skirt around her.

Unless. Unless . . . your father's cloak.

She looks back at the map, she looks at the boys. She smiles to herself.

Well, if I didn't see you, I didn't see you.

She exits. The two boys remove the cloak. They sit in silence for a moment.

ALBUS
Yes, I stole this from James. He's remarkably easy to steal from, his trunk combination is the date he got his first broom. I've found the cloak made avoiding bullies easier.

SCORPIUS *nods.*

I'm sorry – about your mum. I know we don't talk about her enough – but I hope you know – I'm sorry – it's rubbish – what happened to her – to you.

SCORPIUS
Thanks.

ALBUS
My dad said – said that you were this dark cloud around me. My dad started to think – and I just knew I had to stay away, and if I didn't, Dad said he would—

SCORPIUS
Your dad thinks the rumours are true – I am the son of Voldemort?

ALBUS *(nods)*
His department are currently investigating it.

SCORPIUS

Good. Let them. Sometimes – sometimes I find myself
thinking – maybe they're true too.

ALBUS

No. They're not true. And I'll tell you why. Because I don't
think Voldemort is capable of having a kind son – and
you're kind, Scorpius. To the depths of your belly, to the
tips of your fingers. I truly believe Voldemort – Voldemort
couldn't have a child like you.

Beat. SCORPIUS *is moved by this.*

SCORPIUS

That's nice – that's a nice thing to say.

ALBUS

And it's something I should have said a long time ago.
In fact, you're probably the best person I know. And
you don't – you couldn't – hold me back – you make me
stronger – and when Dad forced us apart – without you—

SCORPIUS

I didn't much like my life without you in it either.

ALBUS

And I know I'll always be Harry Potter's son – and I will
sort that out in my head – and I know compared to you my
life is pretty good really and that he and I are comparatively
lucky and—

SCORPIUS *(interrupting)*

Albus, as apologies go this is wonderfully fulsome, but
you're starting to talk more about *you* than *me* again, so
probably better to quit while you're ahead.

ALBUS *smiles and stretches out a hand.*

ALBUS

Friends?

SCORPIUS
Always.

SCORPIUS extends his hand, ALBUS pulls SCORPIUS up into a hug.

That's the second time you've done that.

The two boys break apart and smile.

ALBUS
But I'm pleased we had this argument because it's given me a really good idea.

SCORPIUS
About what?

ALBUS
It involves the second task. And humiliation.

SCORPIUS
You're still talking about going back in time? Have we been having the same conversation?

ALBUS
You're right – we are losers. We're brilliant at losing and so we should be using our own knowledge here. Our own powers. Losers are taught to be losers. And there's only one way to teach a loser – and we know that better than anyone – humiliation. We need to humiliate him. So in the second task that's what we'll do.

SCORPIUS thinks – for a long time – and then smiles.

SCORPIUS
That's a really good strategy.

ALBUS
I know.

SCORPIUS
I mean, quite spectacular. Humiliate Cedric to save Cedric. Clever. And Rose?

ALBUS

That I'm saving as a sparkly surprise. I *can* do it without you – but I *want* you there. Because I want us to do this together. Set things right together. So . . . will you come?

SCORPIUS

But, just a minute, isn't – wasn't – the second task took place in the lake and you're not allowed to leave the school building?

ALBUS *grins.*

ALBUS

Yes. About that . . . we need to find the girls' bathroom on the first floor.

ACT TWO   SCENE SEVENTEEN

HOGWARTS, STAIRCASES

RON *is walking down the staircase, consumed, and then he sees* HERMIONE *and his expression changes entirely.*

RON
   Professor Granger.

   HERMIONE *looks across, her heart leaps a bit too (though she won't admit it).*

HERMIONE
   Ron. What are you doing here?

RON
   Panju got in a little trouble in Potions class. Was showing off of course and put the wrong thing with the wrong thing, and now he has no eyebrows and a rather large moustache, apparently. Which doesn't suit him. I didn't want to come but Padma says that when it comes to facial growths, sons need their fathers. Have you done something with your hair?

HERMIONE
   Just combed it I suspect.

RON
   Well . . . combing it suits you.

HERMIONE *looks at* RON *slightly strangely.*

HERMIONE
Ron, will you stop looking at me like that?

RON *(summoning confidence)*
You know, Harry's boy Albus – said to me the other day
that he thought you and I were – married. Ha ha. Ha. Ha.
Ridiculous, I know.

HERMIONE
Very ridiculous.

RON
He even thought we had a daughter. That'd be strange
wouldn't it?

The two lock eyes. HERMIONE *is the first to break away.*

HERMIONE
More than strange.

RON
Exactly. We're – friends and that's all.

HERMIONE
Absolutely. Only – friends.

RON
Only – friends. Funny word – friends. Not that funny. Just
a word really. Friends. Friend. Funny friend. You, my funny
friend, my Hermione. Not that – not *my* Hermione, you
understand – not MY Hermione – not MINE – you know,
but . . .

HERMIONE
I know.

*There's a pause. Neither of them moves the smallest inch.
Everything feels too important for movement. Then* RON
coughs.

RON

Well. Must get on. Sort Panju out. Teach him the finer arts of moustache grooming.

He walks on, he turns, looks at HERMIONE. *She looks back, he hurries on again.*

Your hair really does very much suit you.

———

ACT TWO SCENE EIGHTEEN

HOGWARTS, HEADMISTRESS'S OFFICE

PROFESSOR McGONAGALL *is onstage on her own. She looks at the map. She frowns to herself. She taps it with her wand. She smiles to herself at a good decision made.*

PROFESSOR McGONAGALL
Mischief managed.

> *There's a rattling.*
> *The whole stage seems to vibrate.*
> GINNY *is the first through the fireplace, and then* HARRY.

GINNY
Professor, I can't say that ever gets more dignified.

PROFESSOR McGONAGALL
Potter. You're back. And you seem to have finally ruined my carpet.

HARRY
I need to find my son. We need to.

PROFESSOR McGONAGALL
Harry, I've considered this and decided I want no part of it. Whatever you threaten, I—

HARRY

Minerva, I come here in peace, not war. I should never
have spoken to you that way.

PROFESSOR McGONAGALL

I just don't think I can interfere in friendships and I
believe—

HARRY

I need to say sorry to you and sorry to Albus, will you give
me that chance?

DRACO *arrives behind them with a bang of soot.*

PROFESSOR McGONAGALL

Draco?

DRACO

He needs to see his son, and I need to see mine.

HARRY

Like I say – peace – not war.

PROFESSOR McGONAGALL *studies his face, she sees the*
sincerity she needs to see. She takes the map back out of
her pocket. She opens it up.

PROFESSOR McGONAGALL

Well, peace is certainly something I can be part of.

She taps it with her wand. Sighs.

I solemnly swear that I'm up to no good.

The map is lit into action.

Well, they are together.

DRACO

In the girls' bathroom on the first floor. What on earth
would they be doing there?

ACT TWO SCENE NINETEEN

HOGWARTS, GIRLS' BATHROOM

SCORPIUS *and* ALBUS *enter a bathroom. In the centre of it is a large Victorian sink.*

SCORPIUS

So let me get this right – the plan is Engorgement . . .

ALBUS

Yes. Scorpius, that soap if you may . . .

SCORPIUS *fishes a soap out of the sink.*

Engorgio!

He fires a bolt from his wand across the room. The soap blows up to four times its size.

SCORPIUS

Nice. Consider me engorgimpressed.

ALBUS

The second task was the lake task. They had to retrieve something which was stolen from them, which turned out to be—

SCORPIUS

—people they loved.

ALBUS

Cedric used a Bubble-Head Charm to swim through the lake. All we do is follow him in there, and use Engorgement to turn him into something rather larger. We know the Time-Turner doesn't give us long, so we're going to be quick. Get to him and Engorgio his head and watch him float out of the lake – away from the task – away from the competition . . .

SCORPIUS

But – you still haven't told me how we're going to actually get to the lake . . .

And then suddenly a jet of water emerges from the sink and after it ascends a very wet MOANING MYRTLE.

MOANING MYRTLE

Whoah. That feels good. Never used to enjoy that. But when you get to my age, you take what you can . . .

SCORPIUS

Of course – you're a genius – Moaning Myrtle . . .

MOANING MYRTLE *swoops down on to* SCORPIUS.

MOANING MYRTLE

What did you call me? Do I moan? Am I moaning now? *Am I? Am I?*

SCORPIUS

No, I didn't mean . . .

MOANING MYRTLE

What's my name?

SCORPIUS

Myrtle.

MOANING MYRTLE

Exactly – Myrtle. Myrtle Elizabeth Warren – a pretty name – my name. No need for the Moaning.

SCORPIUS
> Well . . .

MOANING MYRTLE (*she giggles*)
> It's been a while. Boys. In my bathroom. In my girls'
> bathroom. Well, that's not right . . . but then again, I always
> did have a soft spot for the Potters. And I was moderately
> partial to a Malfoy too. Now how can I help you pair?

ALBUS
> You were there Myrtle – in the lake. They wrote about you.
> There must be a way out of these pipes.

MOANING MYRTLE
> I've been everywhere. But where specifically were you
> thinking?

ALBUS
> The second task. The lake task. In the Triwizard
> Tournament. Twenty-five years ago. Harry and Cedric.

MOANING MYRTLE
> Such a shame the pretty one had to die. Not that your
> father is not pretty – but Cedric Diggory – you'd be amazed
> at how many girls I had to hear doing love incantations in
> this very bathroom . . . and the weeping after he was
> taken.

ALBUS
> Help us Myrtle, help us get into that same lake.

MOANING MYRTLE
> You think I can help you travel in time?

ALBUS
> We need you to keep a secret.

MOANING MYRTLE
> I love secrets. I won't tell a soul. Cross my heart and hope to
> die. Or – the equivalent. For ghosts. You know.

ALBUS *nods at* SCORPIUS, *who reveals the Time-Turner.*

ALBUS

We can travel in time. You're going to help us travel the
pipes. We're going to save Cedric Diggory.

MOANING MYRTLE (*grins*)

Well, that sounds like fun.

ALBUS

And we've no time to lose.

MOANING MYRTLE

This very sink. This very sink empties directly into the
lake. It breaks every bylaw but this school has always been
antiquated. Dive in and you will be piped straight to it.

> ALBUS *pulls himself into the sink, dumping his cloak as he
> does.* SCORPIUS *copies.*
>
> ALBUS *hands* SCORPIUS *some green foliage in a bag.*

ALBUS

Some for me and some for you.

SCORPIUS

Gillyweed? We're using Gillyweed? To breathe under water?

ALBUS

Just like my dad did. Now, are you ready?

SCORPIUS

Remember, this time, we can't be caught out by the
clock . . .

ALBUS

Five minutes, that's all we allow for, before we get pulled
back to the present.

SCORPIUS

Tell me this is all going to be okay.

ALBUS (*grinning*)

It's all going to be entirely okay. Are you ready?

> ALBUS *takes the Gillyweed and disappears down.*

SCORPIUS
No, Albus – Albus –

He looks up, he and MOANING MYRTLE *are alone.*

MOANING MYRTLE
I do like brave boys.

SCORPIUS *(a little bit scared, a tiny bit brave)*
Then I'm entirely ready. For whatever comes.

He takes the Gillyweed and disappears down.

MOANING MYRTLE *is left alone onstage.*

There is a giant whoosh of light and smash of noise.
And time stops. And then it turns over, thinks a bit, and
begins spooling backwards . . .

The boys are gone.

HARRY *appears at a run, a deep frown on his face, behind*
him DRACO, GINNY *and* PROFESSOR McGONAGALL.

HARRY
Albus . . . Albus . . .

GINNY
He's gone.

They find the boys' cloaks on the ground.

PROFESSOR McGONAGALL *(consulting the map)*
He's disappeared. No, he's travelling under Hogwarts
grounds, no, he's disappeared—

DRACO
How is he doing this?

MOANING MYRTLE
He's using a rather pretty trinket thingy.

HARRY
Myrtle!

MOANING MYRTLE
Oops, you caught me. And I was trying so hard to hide.

Hello, Harry. Hello, Draco. Have you been bad boys again?

HARRY

What trinket is he using?

MOANING MYRTLE

I think it was a secret, but I could never keep anything from you Harry. How is it you've grown handsomer and handsomer as you've aged? And you're taller.

HARRY

My son is in danger. I need your help. What are they doing Myrtle?

MOANING MYRTLE

He's after saving a dishy boy. A certain Cedric Diggory.

HARRY *immediately realises what's happened, and is horrified.*

PROFESSOR McGONAGALL

But Cedric Diggory died years ago . . .

MOANING MYRTLE

He seemed quite confident he could get around that fact. He's very confident Harry, just like you.

HARRY

He heard me talking – to Amos Diggory . . . could he have . . . the Ministry's Time-Turner. No, that's impossible.

PROFESSOR McGONAGALL

The Ministry has a Time-Turner? I thought they were destroyed?

MOANING MYRTLE

Isn't everyone so naughty?

DRACO

Can someone please explain what's going on?

HARRY

Albus and Scorpius are not disappearing and reappearing – they're travelling. Travelling in time.

ACT TWO   SCENE TWENTY

TRIWIZARD TOURNAMENT, LAKE, 1995

LUDO BAGMAN

Ladies and gentlemen, boys and girls, I give you –
the greatest – the fabulous – the one – and the only
TRIWIZARD TOURNAMENT! If you're from Hogwarts.
Give me a cheer.

There's a loud cheer.

And now ALBUS *and* SCORPIUS *are swimming through
the lake. Descending through the water with graceful
ease.*

If you're from Durmstrang – give me a cheer.

There's a loud cheer.

AND IF YOU'RE FROM BEAUXBATONS GIVE ME A
CHEER.

There's a slightly less limp cheer.

The French are getting into this.

And they're off ... Viktor's a shark, of course he is, Fleur
looks remarkable, ever plucky Harry is using Gillyweed,
clever Harry, very clever – and Cedric – well, Cedric, what

170

a treat ladies and gentlemen, Cedric is using a Bubble
Charm to cruise through the lake.

> CEDRIC DIGGORY *approaches them through the water,*
> *a bubble over his head.* ALBUS *and* SCORPIUS *raise their*
> *wands together and fire an Engorgement Charm through*
> *the water.*
>
> *He turns and looks at them confused. And it hits him.*
> *And around him the water glows gold.*
>
> *And then* CEDRIC *starts to grow – and grow again – and*
> *grow some more.*
>
> *He looks around himself – entirely panicked. And the*
> *boys watch as* CEDRIC *ascends helplessly through the*
> *water.*

But no, what's this ... Cedric Diggory is ascending out of
the water and seemingly out of the competition. Oh, ladies
and gentlemen, we don't have our winner but we certainly
have our loser. Cedric Diggory is turning into a balloon
and this balloon wants to fly. Fly, ladies and gentlemen,
fly. Fly out of the task and out of the tournament and – oh
my, it gets wilder still, around Cedric fireworks *explode*
declaiming – 'Ron loves Hermione' – and the crowd love
that – oh, ladies and gentlemen, the look on Cedric's face.
It's quite some picture, it's quite some sight, it's quite some
tragedy. This is a humiliation, there's no other word for it.

> *And* ALBUS *smiles widely and high-fives* SCORPIUS *in the*
> *water.*
>
> *And* ALBUS *points up, and* SCORPIUS *nods, and they start*
> *to swim ever upward. And as* CEDRIC *ascends people start*
> *to laugh, and everything changes.*
>
> *The world becomes darker. The world becomes almost*
> *black in fact.*
>
> *And there's a flash. And a bang. And the Time-Turner*

ticks to a stop. And we're back in the present.
SCORPIUS *suddenly emerges, shooting up through the*
water. And he's triumphant.

SCORPIUS
Woooo – hoooooo!

He looks around, surprised. Where's Albus? He puts his
arms into the air.

We did it!

He waits another beat.

Albus?

Albus still doesn't emerge. SCORPIUS *treads water, he*
thinks and then he ducks back into the water.
He emerges back up again. Now thoroughly panicked. He
looks around.

Albus ... ALBUS ... ALBUS.

And there's a whisper in Parseltongue. Which travels fast
around the audience. He's coming. He's coming. He's
coming.

DOLORES UMBRIDGE
Scorpius Malfoy. Get out of the lake. Get out of the lake.
Right now.

She pulls him out of the water.

SCORPIUS
Miss. I need help. Please, Miss.

DOLORES UMBRIDGE
Miss? I'm Professor Umbridge, the Headmistress of your
school, I'm no Miss.

SCORPIUS
You're the Headmistress? But I ...

DOLORES UMBRIDGE

I am the Headmistress and however important your family may be – it doesn't give you an excuse to dilly-dally, to mess about.

SCORPIUS

There's a boy in this lake. You need to get help. I'm looking for my friend, Miss. Professor. Headmaster. One of Hogwarts's students, Miss. I'm looking for Albus Potter.

DOLORES UMBRIDGE

Potter? Albus Potter? There's no such student. In fact, there hasn't been a Potter at Hogwarts for years – and that boy didn't turn out so well. Not so much rest in peace, Harry Potter, more rest in perpetual despair. Total troublemaker.

SCORPIUS

Harry Potter's dead?

Suddenly from around the auditorium, the feel of a breath of the wind. Some black robes arise around people. Black robes that become black shapes. That become Dementors.

Flying Dementors through the auditorium. These black deadly shapes, these black deadly forces. They are everything to be feared. And they suck the spirit from the room.

The wind continues. This is Hell. And then right from the back of the room and whispering around everyone. Words said with an unmistakeable voice. The voice of VOLDEMORT . . .

Haaarry Potttttter . . .

Harry's dream has come to life.

DOLORES UMBRIDGE

Have you swallowed something funny in there? Become a Mudblood without any of us noticing? Harry Potter died over twenty years ago as part of that failed coup on the school – he was one of those Dumbledore terrorists we bravely overthrew at the Battle of Hogwarts. Now come along – I don't know what game you're playing but you're upsetting the Dementors and entirely ruining Voldemort Day.

And the Parseltongue whispers grow louder and louder. Grow monstrously loud. And giant banners with snake symbols upon them descend over the stage.

SCORPIUS
Voldemort Day?

We cut to black.

END OF PART ONE

PART TWO

ACT THREE SCENE ONE

HOGWARTS, HEADMISTRESS'S OFFICE

SCORPIUS *enters the office of* DOLORES UMBRIDGE. *He is dressed in darker, blacker robes. He has a pensive look on his face. He remains coiled and alert.*

DOLORES UMBRIDGE
Scorpius. Thank you so much for coming to see me.

SCORPIUS
Headmistress.

DOLORES UMBRIDGE
Scorpius, I've thought for a long time that you have Head Boy potential, as you know. Pure-blooded, a natural leader, wonderfully athletic . . .

SCORPIUS
Athletic?

DOLORES UMBRIDGE
No need to be modest, Scorpius. I've seen you on the Quidditch pitch, there's rarely a Snitch you don't catch. You are a highly valued student. Valued by the faculty. Valued especially by me. I've positively glowed about you in dispatches to the Augurey. Our work together, flushing out the more dilettante students has made this school a safer – purer – place.

SCORPIUS
Has it?

There is the sound of a scream from off. SCORPIUS *turns towards it. But he dismisses the thought. He must and he will control himself.*

DOLORES UMBRIDGE
But in the three days since I found you in that lake on Voldemort Day, you've become . . . odder and odder – in particular, this sudden obsession with Harry Potter . . .

SCORPIUS
I don't . . .

DOLORES UMBRIDGE
Questioning everyone you can about the Battle of Hogwarts. How Potter died. Why Potter died. And this ludicrous fascination with Cedric Diggory. Scorpius – we've checked you for hexes and curses – there were none we can see – so I'm asking if there's anything I can do – to restore you to what you were . . .

SCORPIUS
No. No. Consider me restored. Temporary aberration. That's all.

DOLORES UMBRIDGE
So we can continue our work together?

SCORPIUS
We can.

She puts her hand to her heart, and touches her wrists together.

DOLORES UMBRIDGE
For Voldemort and Valour.

SCORPIUS *(trying to copy)*
For – um – yes.

ACT THREE   SCENE TWO

HOGWARTS, GROUNDS

KARL JENKINS
Hey Scorpion King.

SCORPIUS is high-fived. It's painful, he takes it.

YANN FREDERICKS
We're still on right, tomorrow night?

KARL JENKINS
Because we are ready to spill some proper Mudblood guts.

POLLY CHAPMAN
Scorpius.

POLLY CHAPMAN is standing on the stairs, SCORPIUS turns towards her, surprised to hear her say his name.

SCORPIUS
Polly Chapman?

POLLY CHAPMAN
Shall we cut to it? I know everyone is waiting to know who you're going to ask because, you know, you need to ask someone and I've been asked by three people already and I know I'm not alone in refusing them all. In case, you know, you were to ask me.

SCORPIUS

Right.

POLLY CHAPMAN

Which would be great. If you were interested. Which
rumour is – you are. And I just want to make clear – at
this moment – that I am also interested. And that isn't a
rumour. That's a – f-a-c-t – fact.

SCORPIUS

That's um – great, but – what are we talking about?

POLLY CHAPMAN

The Blood Ball of course – who you – the Scorpion King,
are taking to the Blood Ball.

SCORPIUS

You – Polly Chapman – want me to take you to a – ball?

There is the sound of screaming behind him.

What is that screaming?

POLLY CHAPMAN

Mudbloods of course. In the dungeons. Your idea wasn't it?
What's going on with you? Oh Potter, I've got blood on my
shoes again . . .

She bends and carefully cleans the blood off her shoes.

Like the Augurey insists – the future is ours to make – so
here I am – making a future – with you. For Voldemort and
Valour.

SCORPIUS

For Voldemort it is.

POLLY *walks on,* SCORPIUS *looks agonised after her. What
is this world – and what is he within it?*

ACT THREE   SCENE THREE

MINISTRY OF MAGIC, OFFICE OF THE HEAD OF MAGICAL LAW ENFORCEMENT

DRACO *is impressive in a way we haven't seen. He has the smell of power about him. Flying down either side of the room are Augurey flags – with the bird emblazoned in a fascistic manner.*

DRACO
You are late.

SCORPIUS
This is your office?

DRACO
You are late and unapologetic. Maybe you are determined to compound the problem.

SCORPIUS
You're Head of Magical Law Enforcement?

DRACO
How dare you! How dare you embarrass me and keep me waiting and then not apologise for it!

SCORPIUS
Sorry.

DRACO
Sir.

183

SCORPIUS

Sorry, sir.

DRACO

I did not bring you up to be sloppy, Scorpius. I did not bring you up to humiliate me at Hogwarts.

SCORPIUS

Humiliate you, sir?

DRACO

Harry Potter, asking questions about Harry Potter, of all the embarrassing things. How dare you disgrace the Malfoy name.

SCORPIUS

Oh no. Are you responsible? No. No. You can't be.

DRACO

Scorpius . . .

SCORPIUS

The *Daily Prophet* today – three wizards blowing up bridges to see how many Muggles they can kill with one blast – is that you?

DRACO

Be very careful.

SCORPIUS

The 'Mudblood' death camps, the torture, the burning alive of those that oppose him. How much of that is you? Mum always told me that you were a better man than I could see, but this is what you really are isn't it? A murderer, a torturer, a—

DRACO rises up and pulls SCORPIUS hard on to the table. The violence is surprising and deadly.

DRACO

Do not use her name in vain, Scorpius. Do not score points that way. She deserves better than that.

SCORPIUS *says nothing. Horrified and scared.* DRACO
reads this. He lets go of SCORPIUS's *head. He doesn't like
hurting his son.*

And no, those idiots blasting Muggles, that's not my doing,
though it'll be me the Augurey asks to bribe the Muggle
Prime Minister with gold . . . Did your mother really say
that of me?

SCORPIUS
She said that grandfather didn't like her very much –
opposed the match – thought she was too Muggle-loving –
too weak – but that you defied him for her. She said it was
the bravest thing she'd ever seen.

DRACO
She made being brave very easy, your mother.

SCORPIUS
But that was – another you.

He looks at his dad, who looks back with a frown.

I've done bad things, you've done worse. What have we
become, Dad?

DRACO
We haven't become anything – we simply are as we are.

SCORPIUS
The Malfoys. The family you can always rely on to make
the world a murkier place.

This hits home with DRACO, *he looks carefully at*
SCORPIUS.

DRACO
This business at the school – what's inspired it?

SCORPIUS
I don't want to be who I am.

185

DRACO
And what's brought that on?

SCORPIUS *desperately thinks for a way of describing his story.*

SCORPIUS
I've seen myself in a different way.

DRACO
You know what I loved most about your mother? She could always help me find light in the darkness. She made the world – my world anyway – less – what was the word you used – 'murky'.

SCORPIUS
Did she?

DRACO *studies his son.*

DRACO
There's more of her in there than I thought.

Beat. He looks at SCORPIUS *carefully.*

Whatever you're doing – do it safely. I can't lose you too.

SCORPIUS
Yes. Sir.

DRACO *looks at his son one last time – trying to understand his head.*

DRACO
For Voldemort and Valour.

SCORPIUS *looks at him and backs out of the room.*

SCORPIUS
For Voldemort and Valour.

ACT THREE SCENE FOUR

HOGWARTS, LIBRARY

SCORPIUS *enters the library and starts to desperately look through books. He finds a history book.*

SCORPIUS
How did Cedric become a Death Eater? What have I missed? Find me some – light in the darkness.

CRAIG BOWKER JR
Why are you here?

> SCORPIUS *turns to look at a rather desperate-looking* CRAIG, *his clothes tattered and worn.*

SCORPIUS
Why can't I be here?

CRAIG BOWKER JR
It's not ready yet. I'm working as fast as I can. But Professor Snape sets so much of it, and writing the essay in two different ways. I mean, I'm not complaining . . . sorry.

SCORPIUS
Start again. From the beginning. What's not ready?

CRAIG BOWKER JR
Your Potions homework. And I'm happy to do it – grateful

even – and I know you hate homework and books, and I
never let you down, you know that.

SCORPIUS

I hate homework?

CRAIG BOWKER JR

You're the Scorpion King. Of course you hate homework.
What are you doing with A *History of Magic*? I could do
that assignment too?

Pause. SCORPIUS *looks at* CRAIG *a moment and then
walks away.* CRAIG *exits.*

After a moment SCORPIUS *returns with a frown.*

SCORPIUS

Did he say Snape?

ACT THREE   SCENE FIVE

HOGWARTS, POTIONS CLASSROOM

SCORPIUS *runs into the Potions classroom. Slamming back the door.* SEVERUS SNAPE *looks up at him.*

SNAPE
Did no one teach you to knock, boy?

SCORPIUS *looks up at* SNAPE, *slightly breathless, slightly unsure, slightly exultant.*

SCORPIUS
Severus Snape. This is an honour.

SNAPE
Professor Snape will do fine. You may behave like a king at this school Malfoy, but that doesn't make us all your subjects.

SCORPIUS
But you're the answer . . .

SNAPE
How very pleasant for me. If you've got something to say boy, then please say it . . . if not, close the door on your way out.

SCORPIUS
I need your help.

SNAPE

I exist to serve.

SCORPIUS

I just don't know what help I – need. Are you still undercover now? Are you still working secretly for Dumbledore?

SNAPE

Dumbledore? Dumbledore's dead. And my work for him was public – I taught in his school.

SCORPIUS

No. That's not all you did. You watched the Death Eaters for him. You advised him. Everyone thought you'd murdered him – but it turned out you'd been supporting him. You saved the world.

SNAPE

These are very dangerous allegations, boy. And don't think the Malfoy name will prevent me inflicting punishment.

SCORPIUS

What if I was to tell you there was another world – another world in which Voldemort was defeated at the Battle of Hogwarts, in which Harry Potter and Dumbledore's Army won, how would you feel then . . .

SNAPE

I'd say that the rumours of Hogwarts's beloved Scorpion King losing his mind are well founded.

SCORPIUS

There was a stolen Time-Turner. I stole a Time-Turner. With Albus. We tried to bring Cedric Diggory back from the dead, when he was dead. We tried to stop him winning the Triwizard Tournament. But by doing so we turned him into an almost different person entirely.

SNAPE

Harry Potter won that Triwizard Tournament.

SCORPIUS

He wasn't supposed to do it alone. Cedric was supposed
to win it with him. But we humiliated him out of the
tournament. And as a result of that humiliation he became
a Death Eater. I can't work out what he did in the Battle
of Hogwarts – whether he killed someone or – but he did
something and it changed everything.

SNAPE

Cedric Diggory killed only one wizard and not a significant
one – Neville Longbottom.

SCORPIUS

Oh, of course, that's it! Professor Longbottom was supposed
to kill Nagini, Voldemort's snake. Nagini had to die
before Voldemort could die. That's it! You've solved it! We
destroyed Cedric, he killed Neville, Voldemort won the
battle. Can you see? Can you see it?

SNAPE

I can see this is a Malfoy game. Get out before I alert your
father and plunge you into deep trouble.

SCORPIUS *thinks and then plays his final, desperate, card.*

SCORPIUS

You loved his mother. I don't remember everything. I know
you loved his mother. Harry's mother. Lily. I know you
spent years undercover. I know without you the war could
never have been won. How would I know this if I hadn't
seen the other world . . . ?

SNAPE *says nothing, overwhelmed.*

Only Dumbledore knew, am I right? And when you lost
him you must have felt so alone. I know you're a good man.
Harry Potter told his son you're a great man.

SNAPE *looks at* SCORPIUS, *unsure what's going on. Is this a trick? He is quite seriously at a loss.*

SNAPE

Harry Potter is dead.

SCORPIUS

Not in my world. He said you were the bravest man he'd ever met. He knew, you see – he knew your secret – what you did for Dumbledore. And he admired you for it – greatly. And that's why he named his son – my best friend – after you both. Albus Severus Potter.

SNAPE *is stopped. He is deeply moved.*

Please – for Lily, for the world, help me.

SNAPE *thinks and then walks up to* SCORPIUS, *taking out his wand as he does.* SCORPIUS *steps back, scared.* SNAPE *fires his wand at the door.*

SNAPE

Colloportus!

An invisible lock slams into place. SNAPE *opens a hatch at the back of the classroom.*

Well, come on then . . .

SCORPIUS

Just a question, but where – exactly – are we going?

SNAPE

We've had to move many times. Everywhere we've settled they destroyed. This will take us to a room hidden in the roots of the Whomping Willow.

SCORPIUS

Okay, who's we?

SNAPE

Oh. You'll see.

ACT THREE SCENE SIX

CAMPAIGN ROOM

SCORPIUS *is pinned to the table by a rather magnificent-looking* HERMIONE. *Her clothes faded, her eyes blazing, she is full warrior now and it rather suits her.*

HERMIONE
You make one more move and your brain will be a frog and your arms will be rubber.

SNAPE
Safe. He's safe. (*Beat.*) You know you never could listen. You were a terrible bore of a student and you're a terrible bore of – whatever you are.

HERMIONE
I was an excellent student.

SNAPE
You were moderate to average. He's on our side!

SCORPIUS
I am, Hermione.

HERMIONE *looks at* SCORPIUS, *still very distrustful.*

HERMIONE
Most people know me as Granger. And I don't believe a word you say, Malfoy.

SCORPIUS
It's all my fault. My fault. And Albus's.

HERMIONE
Albus? Albus Dumbledore? What's Albus Dumbledore got to do with this?

SNAPE
He doesn't mean Dumbledore. You may need to sit down.

RON runs in. His hair spiked. His clothes scruffy. He is slightly less good at the rebel look than HERMIONE is.

RON
Snape, a royal visit and – (*he sees* SCORPIUS, *and is immediately alarmed*) what's he doing here?

He fumbles out his wand.

I'm armed and – entirely dangerous and seriously advise you—

He realises his wand is around the wrong way and turns it right.

—to be very careful—

SNAPE
He's safe, Ron.

RON looks at HERMIONE, *who nods.*

RON
Thank Dumbledore for that.

ACT THREE   SCENE SEVEN

CAMPAIGN ROOM

HERMIONE *is sitting studying the Time-Turner as* RON *tries to digest it all.*

RON
So you're telling me that the whole of history rests on . . . Neville Longbottom? This is pretty wild.

HERMIONE
It's true, Ron.

RON
Right. And you're sure because . . .

HERMIONE
What he knows about Snape – about all of us – there's no way he could . . .

RON
Maybe he's a really good guesser?

SCORPIUS
I'm not. Can you help?

RON
We're the only ones that can. Dumbledore's Army has shrunk considerably since its peak, in fact, we're pretty much all that's left, but we've kept fighting on. Hiding

in plain sight. Doing our best to tickle their nose hairs. Granger here is a wanted woman. I'm a wanted man.

SNAPE (*dryly*)
Less-wanted.

HERMIONE
To be clear: in this other world . . . before you meddled?

SCORPIUS
Voldemort is dead. Killed in the Battle of Hogwarts. Harry is Head of Magical Law Enforcement. You're Minister for Magic.

HERMIONE stops, surprised by this, she looks up with a smile.

HERMIONE
I'm Minister for Magic?

RON (*wanting to join the fun*)
Brilliant. What do I do?

SCORPIUS
You run Weasleys' Wizard Wheezes.

RON
Okay, so, she's Minister for Magic and I run a – joke shop?

SCORPIUS looks at RON's hurt face.

SCORPIUS
You're mostly focused on bringing up your kids.

RON
Great. I expect their mother is hot.

SCORPIUS (*blushing*)
Well . . . um . . . depends what you think of . . . the thing is, you two, sort of have kids – together. A daughter and a son.

The two look up, astonished.

Married. In love. Everything. You were shocked the other time too. When you were Defence Against the Dark Arts teacher and Ron was married to Padma. You're *constantly* surprised by it.

> HERMIONE *and* RON *both look at each other and then look away. And then* RON *looks back.* RON *clears his throat repeatedly. With less conviction each time.*

HERMIONE
Close your mouth when you're looking at me, Weasley.

> RON *does so. Though he remains discombobulated.*

And – Snape? What does Snape do in this other world?

SNAPE
I'm dead, presumably.

> *He looks at* SCORPIUS. SCORPIUS's *face drops,* SNAPE *smiles thinly.*

You were a little too surprised to see me. How?

SCORPIUS
Bravely.

SNAPE
Who?

SCORPIUS
Voldemort.

SNAPE
How very irritating.

> *There's a silence as* SNAPE *digests this.*

Still, there's glory in being taken down by the Dark Lord himself, I suppose.

HERMIONE
I'm sorry, Severus.

> SNAPE *looks at her, and then swallows the pain. He indicates* RON *with a flick of his head.*

SNAPE

Well, at least I'm not married to him.

HERMIONE

Which spells did you use?

SCORPIUS

Expelliarmus in the first task and Engorgio in the second.

RON

Simple Shield Charms should set both of those right.

SNAPE

And then you left?

SCORPIUS

The Time-Turner took us back, yes. That's the thing – this Time-Turner, you only get five minutes in the past.

HERMIONE

And can you still only move in time not space?

SCORPIUS

Yes, yes, it's – uh – you travel back in the same spot you stand in—

HERMIONE

Interesting.

SNAPE *and* HERMIONE *both know what this means.*

SNAPE

Then it's just me and the boy.

HERMIONE

No offence, Snape, but I'm not trusting this to anyone . . . it's too important.

SNAPE

Hermione, you're the most wanted rebel in the wizarding world. Doing this will require you to go outside. When was the last time you were outside?

HERMIONE

Not for a long time but—

SNAPE

If you're found outside, the Dementors will kiss you – they'll suck out your soul . . .

HERMIONE

Severus, I'm done with living off scraps, making failed attempts at coups, this is our chance to reset the world.

She nods at RON, *who pulls down a map.*

The first task of the tournament took place at the edge of the Forbidden Forest. We turn time here, get to the tournament – block the spell and then return safely. With precision – it can be done and it won't require us to show our faces outside in our time at all. Then we'll turn time again, make our way to the lake, and reverse the second task.

SNAPE

You're risking everything—

HERMIONE

We get this right, Harry's alive, Voldemort's dead and the Augurey is gone. For that no risk is too great. Though I am sorry what it will cost you.

SNAPE

Sometimes costs are made to be borne.

The two look at each other, SNAPE *nods,* HERMIONE *nods back,* SNAPE's *face crumbles slightly.*

I didn't just quote Dumbledore, did I?

HERMIONE (*with a smile*)

No, I'm pretty sure that's pure Severus Snape.

She turns to SCORPIUS, *she indicates the Time-Turner.*

Malfoy.

SCORPIUS *brings her the Time-Turner. She smiles at it,*

excited to use a Time-Turner again, excited to use it for this.

Let's hope this works.

She takes the Time-Turner, it begins to vibrate, and then it explodes into a storm of movement.

And there is a giant whoosh of light. A smash of noise.

And time stops. And then it turns over, thinks a bit, and begins spooling backwards, slow at first . . .

There is a bang and a flash, and our gang disappears.

ACT THREE SCENE EIGHT

EDGE OF THE FORBIDDEN FOREST, 1994

And we watch our scene from Part One replayed, but at the back of the stage rather than the front. We pick out ALBUS *and* SCORPIUS *in their Durmstrang robes. And through it all we hear the 'brilliant' (his words again)* LUDO BAGMAN.

SCORPIUS, HERMIONE, RON *and* SNAPE *watch out anxiously.*

LUDO BAGMAN
And Cedric Diggory has entered the stage. And he seems ready. Scared but ready. He dodges this way. He dodges that. The girls swoon as he dives for cover. They cry as one: don't damage our Diggory, Mr Dragon. And Cedric skirts left and he dives right – and he readies his wand—

SNAPE
This is taking too long. The Time-Turner is spinning.

LUDO BAGMAN
What has this young, brave, handsome man got up his sleevies now?

As ALBUS *attempts to summon Cedric's wand,* HERMIONE *blocks his spell. He looks at his wand, disconsolate, unsure why it hasn't worked.*

And then the Time-Turner spins and they look at it and panic as they're pulled into it.

A dog – he's transfigured a stone into a dog – dog diggity Cedric Diggory – you are a doggy dynamo.

ACT THREE SCENE NINE

EDGE OF THE FORBIDDEN FOREST

They are returned from time, at the edge of the forest, and RON *is in a lot of pain.* SNAPE *looks around, immediately aware of the mess they're in.*

RON

Ow. Ow. Owwwwwww.

HERMIONE

Ron ... Ron ... what has it done to you?

SNAPE

Oh no, I knew it.

SCORPIUS

The Time-Turner did something to Albus too. The first time we went back.

RON

Useful – time to – ow – tell us.

SNAPE

We're above ground. We need to move. Now.

HERMIONE

Ron, you can still walk, come on ...

> RON *does stand up, shouting in pain.* SNAPE *raises his wand.*

SCORPIUS
Did it work?

HERMIONE
We blocked the spell. Cedric kept his wand. Yes. It worked.

SNAPE
But we came back to the wrong place – we are outside. You are outside.

RON
We need to use the Time-Turner again – get out of here—

SNAPE
We need to find shelter. We're horribly exposed.

Suddenly from around the auditorium, the feel of the breath of an icy wind.

Some black robes arise around people. Black robes that become black shapes. That become Dementors.

HERMIONE
Too late.

SNAPE
This is a disaster.

HERMIONE (*she realises what she has to do*)
They're after me, not any of you.

Ron. I love you and I always have. But the three of you need to run. Go. Now.

RON
What?

SCORPIUS
What?

RON
Can we talk about the love thing first?

HERMIONE
This is still Voldemort's world. And I am done with it. Reversing the next task will change everything.

SCORPIUS

But they'll kiss you. They'll suck out your soul.

HERMIONE

And then you'll change the past. And then they won't. Go.
Now.

*The Dementors sense them. From all sides screaming
shapes descend.*

SNAPE

Go! We go.

He pulls on SCORPIUS's *arm.* SCORPIUS *reluctantly goes
with him.*

HERMIONE *looks at* RON.

HERMIONE

You're supposed to be going, too.

RON

Well, they are after me a bit and I really am in quite a lot of
pain. And, you know, I'd rather be here. Expecto—

As he reaches up to cast the spell, HERMIONE *stops his
arm.*

HERMIONE

Let's keep them here and give the boy the best chance we
can.

RON *looks at her and then nods sadly.*

HERMIONE

A daughter.

RON

And a son. I liked that idea too.

He looks around – he knows his fate.

I'm scared.

HERMIONE
Kiss me.

RON *thinks and then does. And then the two are yanked apart. And pinned to the ground. And we watch as a golden-whitish haze is pulled from their bodies. They have their souls sucked from them. And it is terrifying.*

SCORPIUS *watches – helplessly.*

SNAPE
Let's get down to the water. Walk. Don't run.

SNAPE *looks at* SCORPIUS.

Stay calm, Scorpius. They may be blind but they can sense your fear.

SCORPIUS *looks at* SNAPE.

SCORPIUS
They just sucked out their souls.

A Dementor swoops down low over them and settles in front of SCORPIUS.

SNAPE
Think of something else, Scorpius. Occupy your thoughts.

SCORPIUS
I feel cold. I can't see. There's a fog inside me – around me.

SNAPE
You're a king, and I'm a professor. They'll only attack with good reason. Think about those you love, think about why you're doing this.

SCORPIUS
I can hear my mother. She wants me – my – help but she knows I can't – help.

SNAPE

Listen to me, Scorpius. Think about Albus. You're giving up your kingdom for Albus, right?

SCORPIUS *is helpless. Consumed by all the Dementor is making him feel.*

SNAPE

One person. All it takes is one person. I couldn't save Harry for Lily. So now I give my allegiance to the cause she believed in. And it's possible – that along the way I started believing in it myself.

SCORPIUS *smiles at* SNAPE. *He steps decisively away from the Dementor.*

SCORPIUS

The world changes and we change with it. I am better off in this world. But the world is not better. And I don't want that.

Suddenly DOLORES UMBRIDGE *emerges in front of them.*

DOLORES UMBRIDGE

Professor Snape!

SNAPE

Professor Umbridge.

DOLORES UMBRIDGE

Have you heard the news? We've caught that traitorous Mudblood Hermione Granger. She was just out here.

SNAPE

That's – fantastic.

DOLORES *is staring at* SNAPE. *He looks back.*

DOLORES UMBRIDGE

With you. Granger was with you.

SNAPE
　　With me? You're mistaken.

DOLORES UMBRIDGE
　　With you and Scorpius Malfoy. A student I'm becoming increasingly concerned about.

SCORPIUS
　　Well . . .

SNAPE
　　Dolores, we're late for class, so if you'll excuse us . . .

DOLORES UMBRIDGE
　　If you're late for class, why are you not heading back to the school? Why are you heading to the lake?

　　　There's a moment of pure silence. And then SNAPE *does something hugely unusual – he smiles.*

SNAPE
　　How long have you suspected?

　　　DOLORES UMBRIDGE *rises off the ground. She opens her arms wide, full of Dark Magic. She takes out her wand.*

DOLORES UMBRIDGE
　　Years. And I should have acted upon it far earlier.

　　　SNAPE *is faster with his wand.*

SNAPE
　　Depulso!

　　　DOLORES *is propelled backwards through the air.*

　　She always was too grand for her own good. There's no turning back now.

　　　The sky turns even blacker still around them.

　　Expecto Patronum!

SNAPE *sends forward a Patronus, and it's a beautiful white*
shape of a doe.

SCORPIUS

A doe? Lily's Patronus.

SNAPE

Strange isn't it? What comes from within.

Dementors start to appear all around them. SNAPE *knows*
what this means.

You need to run. I will keep them at bay for as long as I can.

SCORPIUS

Thank you for being my light in the darkness.

SNAPE *looks at him, every inch a hero, he softly smiles.*

SNAPE

Tell Albus – tell Albus Severus – I'm proud he carries my
name. Now go. Go!

The doe looks back at SCORPIUS, *and then starts to run.*
SCORPIUS *thinks and then runs after the doe and around*
him the world gets scarier. A blood-curdling scream goes
up at one side. He sees the lake and throws himself
inside.

SNAPE *readies himself.*

SNAPE *is pulled hard to the ground and then pushed*
high into the air as his soul is ripped from him. And the
screams just seem to multiply.

The doe turns to him, with beautiful eyes and disappears.
There is a bang and a flash. And then silence. And then
there's more silence.

It's so still, it's so peaceful, it's so perfectly tranquil.

And then SCORPIUS *ascends to the surface. Breathing*
deeply. He looks around himself. Breathing deep,

panicked breaths. He looks up at the sky. The sky
certainly seems – bluer than before.

And then ALBUS *ascends after him. There's a silence.*
SCORPIUS *just looks at* ALBUS, *disbelieving. Both boys*
breathe in and out.

ALBUS

Whoah!

SCORPIUS

Albus!

ALBUS

That was close! Did you see that Merman? The guy with
the – and then the thing with the – whoah!

SCORPIUS

It's you!

ALBUS

It was weird though – I thought I saw Cedric start to
expand – but then he sort of started shrinking again – and
I looked at you and you had your wand out . . .

SCORPIUS

You have no idea how good it is to see you again.

ALBUS

You just saw me two minutes ago.

SCORPIUS *hugs* ALBUS *in the water, a difficult task.*

SCORPIUS

A lot has happened since then.

ALBUS

Careful. You're drowning me. What are you wearing?

SCORPIUS

What am I wearing? (*He pulls off his cloak.*) What are you
wearing? Yes! You're in Slytherin.

ALBUS

Did it work? Did we do anything?

SCORPIUS
No. And it's brilliant.

ALBUS *looks at him – disbelieving.*

ALBUS
What? We failed.

SCORPIUS
Yes. YES. AND IT'S AMAZING.

He splashes hard in the water. ALBUS *pulls himself out to the bank.*

ALBUS
Scorpius. Have you been eating too many sweets again?

SCORPIUS
There you go you see – all dry humour and Albus-y. I love it.

ALBUS
Now I'm starting to get worried . . .

HARRY *enters and sprints to the side of the water. Followed quickly by* DRACO, GINNY *and* PROFESSOR McGONAGALL.

HARRY
Albus. Albus. Are you okay?

SCORPIUS (*overjoyed*)
Harry! It's Harry Potter! And Ginny. And Professor McGonagall. And Dad. My dad. Hi. Dad.

DRACO
Hello, Scorpius.

ALBUS
You're all here.

GINNY
And Myrtle told us everything.

ALBUS
What is going on?

PROFESSOR McGONAGALL
You're the one who's just returned from time. Why don't you tell us?

SCORPIUS *immediately registers what they know.*

SCORPIUS
Oh no. Oh bother. Where is it?

ALBUS
Just returned from where?

SCORPIUS
I've lost it! I've lost the Time-Turner.

ALBUS *(looking at* SCORPIUS, *deeply annoyed)*
You've lost what?

HARRY
Time to cut the pretence, Albus.

PROFESSOR McGONAGALL
I think you've got some explaining to do.

ACT THREE SCENE TEN

HOGWARTS, HEADMISTRESS'S OFFICE

DRACO, GINNY and HARRY *stand behind a contrite-looking* SCORPIUS *and* ALBUS. PROFESSOR McGONAGALL *is fuming.*

PROFESSOR McGONAGALL

So to be clear – you illegally jumped off the Hogwarts Express, you invaded and stole from the Ministry of Magic, you took it upon yourself to change time, whereupon you disappeared two people—

ALBUS

I agree it doesn't sound good.

PROFESSOR McGONAGALL

And your response to disappearing Hugo and Rose Granger-Weasley was to go back in time again – and this time – instead of losing two people you lost a huge number of people and killed your father – and in doing so you resurrected the worst wizard the world has ever known and heralded in a new age of Dark Magic. (*Dry.*) You're correct, Mr Potter, it doesn't sound good does it? Are you aware how stupid you've been?

SCORPIUS

Yes, Professor.

ALBUS *hesitates a moment. He looks at* HARRY.

ALBUS
  Yes.

HARRY
  Professor, if I may—

PROFESSOR McGONAGALL
  You may not. What you choose to do as parents is your
  matter, but this is my school, and these are my students,
  and I will choose what punishment they will face.

DRACO
  Seems fair.

  HARRY *looks at* GINNY, *who shakes her head.*

PROFESSOR McGONAGALL
  I should expel you but *(with a look to* HARRY*)* all things
  considered – I think it might be safer for you to remain in
  my care. You are in detention for – well, you can consider
  yourself in detention for the rest of the year. Christmas is
  cancelled for you. You can forget visiting Hogsmeade ever
  again. And that's just the start . . .

  Suddenly HERMIONE *bursts in. All action and resolve.*

HERMIONE
  What did I miss?

PROFESSOR McGONAGALL *(fierce)*
  It is considered polite to knock when entering a room,
  Hermione Granger, maybe you missed that.

HERMIONE *(realises she's over-stepped)*
  Ah.

PROFESSOR McGONAGALL
  If I could also give a detention to you, Minister, I would.
  Keeping hold of a Time-Turner, of all the stupid things!

HERMIONE
  In my defence—

PROFESSOR McGONAGALL

And in a bookcase. You kept it in a bookcase. It's almost laughable.

HERMIONE

Minerva. *(There is an intake of breath.)* Professor McGonagall—

PROFESSOR McGONAGALL

Your children didn't exist!

HERMIONE *has no reply to that.*

This happened in my school, under my watch. After all that Dumbledore did, I couldn't live with myself . . .

HERMIONE

I know.

PROFESSOR McGONAGALL *composes herself for a moment.*

PROFESSOR McGONAGALL (*to* ALBUS *and* SCORPIUS)

Your intentions to save Cedric were honourable if misguided. And it does sound as if you were brave, Scorpius, and you, Albus, but the lesson even your father sometimes failed to heed is that bravery doesn't forgive stupidity. Always think. Think what's possible. A world controlled by Voldemort is—

SCORPIUS

A horrific world.

PROFESSOR McGONAGALL

You are so young. *(She looks at* HARRY, DRACO, GINNY *and* HERMIONE.*)* You're all so young. You have no idea how dark the wizarding wars got. You were – reckless – with the world some people – some very dear friends of mine and yours – sacrificed a huge amount to create and sustain.

ALBUS

Yes, Professor.

SCORPIUS

 Yes, Professor.

PROFESSOR McGONAGALL

 Go on. Get out. The lot of you. And find me that
 Time-Turner.

ACT THREE   SCENE ELEVEN

HOGWARTS, SLYTHERIN DORMITORY

ALBUS *is sitting in his room.* HARRY *enters and looks at his son, full of anger, but cautious to not let it spill.*

HARRY
Thanks for letting me come up.

ALBUS *turns, he nods at his dad. He's being cautious too.*

No luck, as yet, with the Time-Turner searching. They're negotiating with the Merpeople to dredge the lake.

He sits down, uncomfortably.

This is a nice room.

ALBUS
Green is a soothing colour isn't it? I mean Gryffindor rooms are all well and good, but the trouble with red is – it is said to send you a little mad – not that I'm casting aspersions . . .

HARRY
Can you explain why you tried to do this?

ALBUS
I thought I could – change things – I thought Cedric – it's unfair.

PART TWO

HARRY

Of course it's unfair Albus, don't you think I know that?
I was there. I saw him die. But to do this . . . to risk all
this . . .

ALBUS

I know.

HARRY (*failing to contain his anger*)

If you were trying to do as I did, you went the wrong way
about it. I didn't volunteer for adventure, I was forced
into it. You did something really reckless – something
really stupid and dangerous – something that could have
destroyed everything—

ALBUS

I know. Okay, I know.

> *Pause.* ALBUS *wipes away a tear,* HARRY *notices it and
> takes a breath. He pulls himself back from the brink.*

HARRY

Well, I was wrong too – to think Scorpius was Voldemort's
son. He wasn't a black cloud.

ALBUS

No.

HARRY

And I've locked away the map. You won't see it again. Your
mum left your room exactly as it was when you ran away –
you know that? Wouldn't let me go in – wouldn't let anyone
go in – you really scared her . . . and me.

ALBUS

Really scared you?

HARRY

Yes.

ALBUS

I thought Harry Potter wasn't afraid of anything?

HARRY

Is that how I make you feel?

ALBUS *looks at his dad, trying to figure him out.*

ALBUS

I don't think Scorpius said, but when we returned after failing to fix the first task, I was suddenly in Gryffindor house, nothing was better between us then either – so the fact that I'm in Slytherin – that's not the reason for our problems. It's not just about that.

HARRY

No. I know. It's not just about that.

HARRY *looks at* ALBUS.

Are you okay, Albus?

ALBUS

No.

HARRY

No. Nor me.

ACT THREE SCENE TWELVE

DREAM, GODRIC'S HOLLOW, GRAVEYARD

YOUNG HARRY *stands looking at a gravestone covered in bunches of flowers. He has a small bunch of flowers in his hand.*

AUNT PETUNIA
Go on then, lay down your grotty little flowers and then let's go. I already hate this poxy little village, I don't know why I even had the thought – Godric's Hollow, Godless Hollow more like, the place is clearly a hive of filth – go on, chop chop.

YOUNG HARRY *approaches the grave. He stands a moment more.*

Now, Harry . . . I don't have time for this. Duddy has his Cubs tonight and you know he hates to be late.

YOUNG HARRY
Aunt Petunia. We're their last living relatives, right?

AUNT PETUNIA
Yes. You and I. Yes.

YOUNG HARRY
And – they weren't popular? You said they didn't have any friends?

AUNT PETUNIA

Lily tried – bless her – she tried – it wasn't her fault, but she repelled people – by her very nature. It was her intensity, it was her – manner, it was her – way. And your father – obnoxious man – extraordinarily obnoxious. No friends. Neither of them.

YOUNG HARRY

So my question is – why are there so many flowers? Why are there flowers all over their grave?

AUNT PETUNIA *looks around, she sees all the flowers as if for the first time and it moves her hugely. She approaches and then sits by her sister's grave, trying hard to fight the emotions as they come to her but succumbing all the same.*

AUNT PETUNIA

Oh. Yes. Well, I suppose there are a – few. Must have blown over from the other graves. Or someone's playing a trick. Yes, I think that's most likely, some young rapscallion with too much time on his hands, has gone around collecting flowers from all the other graves and deposited them here—

YOUNG HARRY

But they're all marked with their names . . . Lily and James, what you did, we will never forget . . . Lily and James, your sacrifice—

VOLDEMORT

I smell guilt, there is a stench of guilt upon the air.

AUNT PETUNIA (*to* YOUNG HARRY)

Get away. Get away from there.

She pulls him back. VOLDEMORT's *hand rises into the air above the Potters' gravestone, the rest of him rises after. We don't see his face but his body provides a jagged, horrific shape.*

I knew it. This place is dangerous. The sooner we leave
Godric's Hollow the better.

YOUNG HARRY *is pulled from the stage, but turns to face*
VOLDEMORT.

VOLDEMORT
Do you still see with my eyes, Harry Potter?

YOUNG HARRY *exits disturbed as* ALBUS *bursts from within*
VOLDEMORT's *cloak. He reaches out a desperate hand*
towards his dad.

ALBUS
Dad ... Dad ...

There's some words spoken in Parseltongue.

He's coming. He's coming. He's coming.

And then a scream.

And then right from the back of the room and whispering
around everyone. Words said with an unmistakeable
voice. The voice of VOLDEMORT ...

Haaarry Pottttter ...

ACT THREE SCENE THIRTEEN

HARRY AND GINNY POTTER'S HOUSE, KITCHEN

HARRY *is in a horrible state. Petrified by what he thinks his dreams are telling him.*

GINNY

Harry? Harry? What is it? You were screaming . . .

HARRY

They haven't stopped. The dreams.

GINNY

They weren't likely to stop immediately. It's been a stressful time and—

HARRY

But I was never in Godric's Hollow with Petunia. This doesn't—

GINNY

Harry, you're really scaring me.

HARRY

He's still here, Ginny.

GINNY

Who's still here?

HARRY

Voldemort. I saw Voldemort and Albus.

GINNY

And Albus ... ?

HARRY

He said – Voldemort said – 'I smell guilt, there is a stench of guilt upon the air.' He was talking to me.

HARRY looks at her. He touches his scar. Her face falls.

GINNY

Harry, is Albus still in danger?

HARRY's face grows white.

HARRY

I think we all are.

ACT THREE   SCENE FOURTEEN

HOGWARTS, SLYTHERIN DORMITORY

SCORPIUS *leans ominously over* ALBUS's *bedhead.*

SCORPIUS
Albus ... Psst ... Albus.

ALBUS *doesn't wake.*

ALBUS!

ALBUS *wakes with a shock.* SCORPIUS *laughs.*

ALBUS
Pleasant. That's a pleasant and not scary way to wake
up.

SCORPIUS
You know it's the strangest of things but ever since being
in the scariest place imaginable I'm pretty much good with
fear. I am – Scorpius the Dreadless. I am – Malfoy the
Unanxious.

ALBUS
Good.

SCORPIUS
I mean, normally, being in lockdown, being in constant
detention. It'd break me but now – what's the worst they

can do? Bring back Mouldy Voldy and have him torture me?
Nope.

ALBUS

You're scary when you're in a good mood, you know that?

SCORPIUS

When Rose came up to me today in Potions and called
me Bread Head, I almost hugged her. No, there's no almost
about it, I actually tried to hug her, and then she kicked me
in the shin.

ALBUS

I'm not sure being fearless is going to be good for your
health.

    SCORPIUS *looks at* ALBUS; *his face grows more*
    contemplative.

SCORPIUS

You don't know how good it is to be back here, Albus. I
hated it there.

ALBUS

Apart from the Polly Chapman fancying you bits.

SCORPIUS

Cedric was a different person entirely – dark, dangerous.
My dad – doing anything they wanted him to. And me?
I discovered another Scorpius you know? Entitled, angry,
mean – people were frightened of me. It feels like we were
all tested and we all – failed.

ALBUS

But you changed things. You had a chance and you
changed time back. Changed yourself back.

SCORPIUS

Only because I knew what I should be.

    ALBUS *digests this.*

ALBUS

Do you think I've been tested too? I have, haven't I?

SCORPIUS

No. Not yet.

ALBUS

You're wrong. The stupid thing wasn't going back once –
anyone can make that mistake – the stupid thing was being
arrogant enough to go back twice.

SCORPIUS

We both went back, Albus.

ALBUS

And why was I so determined to do this? Cedric? Really?
No. I had something to prove. My dad's right – he didn't
volunteer for adventure – me, this, it's all my fault – and if it
wasn't for you everything could have gone Dark.

SCORPIUS

But it didn't. And you're to thank for that as much as me.
When the Dementors were – inside my head – Severus
Snape told me to think of you. You may not have been
there Albus, but you were fighting – fighting alongside me.

ALBUS *nods. Touched by this.*

And saving Cedric – that wasn't such a bad idea – not
in my head anyway – though, you know right – that we
definitely can't try again.

ALBUS

Yes. I do. I do know that.

SCORPIUS

Good. Then you can help me destroy this.

SCORPIUS *reveals the Time-Turner to* ALBUS.

ALBUS

I'm pretty sure you told everyone that was on the bottom of
a lake.

SCORPIUS

Turns out Malfoy the Unanxious is a pretty good liar.

ALBUS

Scorpius, we should tell someone about this . . .

SCORPIUS

Who? The Ministry kept it before, do you really trust them not to keep it again? Only you and I have experienced how dangerous this is, that means you and I have to destroy it. No one can do what we did Albus. No one. No, *(slightly grandly)* it's time that time-turning became a thing of the past.

ALBUS

You're quite proud of that phrase, aren't you?

SCORPIUS

Been working on it all day.

ACT THREE   SCENE FIFTEEN

HOGWARTS, SLYTHERIN DORMITORY

HARRY *and* GINNY *move quickly through the dormitory.* CRAIG BOWKER JR *trails after them.*

CRAIG BOWKER JR
Can I repeat again? This is against the rules and it's the middle of the night.

HARRY
I need to find my son.

CRAIG BOWKER JR
I know who you are, Mr Potter, but even you must understand that it's against school covenant for parents or professors to enter a house quarters without express permission from . . .

PROFESSOR McGONAGALL *charges in behind them.*

PROFESSOR McGONAGALL
Please don't be tiresome, Craig.

HARRY
You got our message? Good.

CRAIG BOWKER JR *(shocked)*
Headmistress. I'm – I was just—

HARRY *pulls open a bed curtain.*

PROFESSOR McGONAGALL
He's gone?

HARRY
Yes.

PROFESSOR McGONAGALL
And young Malfoy?

GINNY *pulls open another.*

GINNY
Oh no.

PROFESSOR McGONAGALL
Then let's turn this school upside down. Craig, we've work
to do . . .

GINNY *and* HARRY *stay looking at the bed.*

GINNY
Haven't we been here before?

HARRY
Something feels even worse this time.

GINNY *looks at her husband, full of fear.*

GINNY
You spoke to him earlier?

HARRY
Yes.

GINNY
You came to his dorm and talked to him?

HARRY
You know I did.

GINNY
What did you say to our son, Harry?

HARRY *can hear the accusation in her voice.*

HARRY

I tried to be honest like you said – I didn't say anything.

GINNY

And you controlled yourself? How heated did it get?

HARRY

... I don't think I ... you think I've scared him away again?

GINNY

I can forgive you for one mistake Harry, maybe even two, but the more mistakes you make, the harder to forgive you it becomes.

ACT THREE   SCENE SIXTEEN

HOGWARTS, OWLERY

SCORPIUS *and* ALBUS *emerge on to a roof bathed in silver light. There's soft hooting all around them.*

SCORPIUS
So, I think a simple Confringo.

ALBUS
Definitely not. For something like this you need Expulso.

SCORPIUS
Expulso? Expulso and we'll be clearing bits of Time-Turner from this owlery for days.

ALBUS
Bombarda?

SCORPIUS
And wake up everyone in Hogwarts? Maybe Stupefy. They were originally destroyed using Stupefy . . .

ALBUS
Exactly, it's been done before – let's do something new, something fun.

SCORPIUS
Fun? Look, many wizards overlook the importance of choosing the right spell but this really matters. I think it's a much-underestimated part of modern witchcraft.

DELPHI

'A much-underestimated part of modern witchcraft' – you two are the greatest, you know that?

SCORPIUS *looks up, surprised to see* DELPHI *has emerged behind them.*

SCORPIUS

Wow. You're ... um ... what are you doing here?

ALBUS

It felt important to send an owl – let her know what we're doing – you know?

SCORPIUS *looks at his friend accusingly.*

This concerns her too.

SCORPIUS *thinks, and then nods, accepting this.*

DELPHI

What concerns me? What's this about?

ALBUS *gets out the* Time-Turner.

ALBUS

We need to destroy the Time-Turner. The things Scorpius saw after the second task ... I'm so sorry. We can't risk going back again. We can't save your cousin.

DELPHI *looks at it and then at them both.*

DELPHI

Your owl said so little ...

ALBUS

Imagine the worst possible world, and then double it. People being tortured – Dementors everywhere – a despotic Voldemort – my dad dead, me never born, the world surrounded by Dark Magic. We just – we can't allow that to happen.

DELPHI *hesitates. And then her face breaks.*

DELPHI
Voldemort ruled? He was alive?

SCORPIUS
He ruled everything. It was terrible.

DELPHI
Because of what we did?

SCORPIUS
Humiliating Cedric turned him into a very angry young man and then he became a Death Eater and – and – it all went wrong. Really wrong.

DELPHI *looks at* SCORPIUS's *face carefully. Her face sinks.*

DELPHI
A Death Eater?

SCORPIUS
And a murderer. He killed Professor Longbottom.

DELPHI
Then – of course – we need to destroy it.

ALBUS
You understand?

DELPHI
I'll go further than that – I'll say Cedric would have understood. We'll destroy it together, and then we'll go to my uncle. Explain the situation.

ALBUS
Thank you.

DELPHI *smiles at them sadly, and then takes the Time-Turner. She looks at it and her expression changes slightly.*

Oh, nice mark.

DELPHI
What?

DELPHI's cloak has loosened. An Augurey tattoo is visible on the back of her neck.

ALBUS
On your back. I hadn't noticed it before. The wings. Is that what the Muggles call a tattoo?

DELPHI
Oh. Yes. Well, it's an Augurey.

SCORPIUS
An Augurey?

DELPHI
Haven't you met them in Care of Magical Creatures? They're sinister-looking black birds that cry when rain's coming. Wizards used to believe that the Augurey's cry foretold death. When I was growing up, my guardian kept one in a cage.

SCORPIUS
Your ... guardian?

DELPHI looks at SCORPIUS. Now she has the Time-Turner she's enjoying this game.

DELPHI
She used to say it was crying because it could see I was going to come to a sticky end. She didn't like me much. Euphemia Rowle ... she only took me in for the gold.

ALBUS
Why would you want a tattoo of her bird, then?

DELPHI
It reminds me that the future is mine to make.

ALBUS
Cool. I might get an Augurey tattoo.

SCORPIUS

The Rowles were pretty extreme Death Eaters.

A thousand thoughts whir inside SCORPIUS's *head.*

ALBUS

Come on, let's get destroying . . . Confringo? Stupefy?
Bombarda? Which would you use?

SCORPIUS

Give it back. Give us back the Time-Turner.

DELPHI

What?

ALBUS

Scorpius? What are you doing?

SCORPIUS

I don't believe you ever were ill. Why didn't you come to
Hogwarts? Why are you here now?

DELPHI

I'm trying to bring my cousin back!

SCORPIUS

They called you the Augurey. In – the other world – they
called you the Augurey.

A slow smile grows on DELPHI's *face.*

DELPHI

The Augurey? I rather like that.

ALBUS

Delphi?

She's too quick. Levelling her wand, she repels SCORPIUS.
And she is far stronger – SCORPIUS *tries to keep her back,
but she quickly overpowers him.*

DELPHI

Fulgari!

SCORPIUS's *arms are bound in vicious, luminous cords.*

SCORPIUS

Albus. Run.

ALBUS *looks around, bewildered. And then starts to run.*

DELPHI

Fulgari!

ALBUS *is propelled to the floor, his hands tied by the same brutal binding.*

And that is the first spell I've had to use on you. I thought I'd have to use plenty more. But you're far easier to control than Amos – children, particularly male children, are so naturally pliant aren't they? Now, let's sort this mess out once and for all . . .

ALBUS

But why? But what? But who are you?

DELPHI

Albus. I am the new past.

She pulls ALBUS's *wand from him and snaps it.*

I am the new future.

She pulls SCORPIUS's *wand from him and snaps it.*

I am the answer this world has been looking for.

ACT THREE SCENE SEVENTEEN

MINISTRY OF MAGIC, HERMIONE'S OFFICE

RON *is sitting on* HERMIONE*'s desk, eating porridge.*

RON
I can't get over it really. The fact that in some realities we aren't even, you know, married.

HERMIONE
Ron whatever this is – I've got ten minutes until the goblins show up to talk security at Gringotts—

RON
I mean, we've been together so long – and married for so long – I mean, so long—

HERMIONE
If this is your way of saying you want a marital break Ron, then, to be clear, I will skewer you with this quill.

RON
Shut up. Will you shut up for once? I want to do one of those marriage renewal things I've read about. Marriage renewal. What do you think?

HERMIONE (*melting slightly*)
You want to marry me again?

RON

> Well, we were only young when we did it the first time and
> I got very drunk and – well, to be honest, I can't remember
> much of it and . . . the truth is – I love you Hermione
> Granger – and whatever time says – I'd like the opportunity
> to say so in front of lots of other people. Again. Sober.

> *She looks at him, she smiles, she pulls him to her, she
> kisses him.*

HERMIONE

> You're sweet.

RON

> And you taste of toffee.

> HERMIONE *laughs.* HARRY, GINNY *and* DRACO *walk in on
> them as they move to kiss again. They spring apart.*

HERMIONE

> Harry, Ginny and – I, uh – Draco – how lovely to see you—

HARRY

> The dreams. They've started again, well, they haven't
> stopped.

GINNY

> And Albus is missing. Again.

DRACO

> Scorpius too. We've had McGonagall check the entire
> school. They're gone.

HERMIONE

> I'll get the Aurors summoned immediately, I'll—

RON

> No, you won't, it's all fine. Albus, I saw him last night. It's
> all good.

DRACO

> Where?

They all turn to look at RON, *he's briefly disconcerted but batters on.*

RON

I was having a couple of Firewhiskies with Neville in Hogsmeade – as you do – setting the world to rights – as we do – and we were coming back – quite late, very late, and trying to work out which Floo I could use because when you've had a drink sometimes you don't want to use the tight ones – or the turny ones or—

GINNY

Ron, if you could get to the point before we all strangle you?

RON

He hasn't run away – he's having a quiet moment – he's got himself an older girlfriend—

HARRY

An older girlfriend?

RON

And a cracking one at that – gorgeous silver hair. Saw them on the roof together, near the owlery with Scorpius playing the gooseberry. Nice to see my love potion being used well, I thought.

HARRY *has a thought.*

HARRY

Her hair – was it silver and blue?

RON

That's it – silver, blue – yup.

HARRY

He's talking about Delphi Diggory. Niece of – Amos Diggory.

GINNY

This is about Cedric again?

HARRY *says nothing, thinking fast.* HERMIONE *looks around the room, concerned, and then shouts out of the door.*

HERMIONE
Ethel. Cancel the goblins.

ACT THREE   SCENE EIGHTEEN

ST OSWALD'S HOME FOR OLD WITCHES AND WIZARDS, AMOS'S ROOM

HARRY *walks in, wand outstretched, with* DRACO.

HARRY

Where are they?

AMOS

Harry Potter, and what can I do for you sir? And Draco Malfoy. I am blessed.

HARRY

I know how you've used my son.

AMOS

I've used your son? No. You sir – you used my beautiful son.

DRACO

Tell us – now – where are Albus and Scorpius or face the profoundest consequences.

AMOS

But why would I know where they are?

DRACO

Don't play the senility card with us, old man. We know you've been sending him owls.

AMOS

I've done nothing of the kind.

HARRY

Amos, you're not too old for Azkaban. They were last
seen on the Hogwarts tower with your niece when they
disappeared.

AMOS

I have no idea what you are ... (*He stops, a beat, confused.*)
My niece?

HARRY

There are no depths to which you won't sink are there –
yes, your niece, are you denying she was there under your
express instructions ...

AMOS

Yes, I am – I don't have a niece.

This stops HARRY.

DRACO

Yes, you do, a nurse, works here. Your niece ... Delphini
Diggory.

AMOS

I know I don't have a niece because I never had any
brothers and sisters. And nor did my wife.

DRACO

We need to find out who she is – *now*.

ACT THREE SCENE NINETEEN

HOGWARTS, QUIDDITCH PITCH

We open on DELPHI, *enjoying every second of her changed identity. Where there was discomfort and insecurity, now there's just power.*

ALBUS
What are we doing on the Quidditch pitch?

DELPHI *says nothing.*

SCORPIUS
The Triwizard Tournament. The third task. The maze. This is where the maze was. We're going back for Cedric.

DELPHI
Yes, it is time to spare the spare once and for all. We will go back for Cedric and in doing so we will resurrect the world you saw Scorpius . . .

SCORPIUS
Hell. You want to resurrect hell?

DELPHI
I want a return to pure and strong magic. I want to rebirth the Dark.

SCORPIUS
You want Voldemort's return?

DELPHI

The one true ruler of the wizarding world. He will return. Now you've ensured the first two tasks are a little clogged up with magic – there are at least two visits from the future in both of them and I will not risk being revealed or distracted. The third task is clean, so let's start there, shall we?

ALBUS

We won't stop him – whatever you force us to do – we know he needs to win the tournament with my dad.

DELPHI

I don't just want you to stop him. I want you to humiliate him. He needs to fly out of that maze naked on a broomstick made of purple feather dusters. Humiliation got you there before and it'll get us there again. And the prophecy will be fulfilled.

SCORPIUS

Wasn't aware that there was a prophecy – what prophecy?

DELPHI

You have seen the world as it should be Scorpius, and today we're going to ensure its return.

ALBUS

We won't. We won't obey you. Whoever you are. Whatever you want us to do.

DELPHI

Of course you will.

ALBUS

You'll have to use Imperio. You'll have to control me.

DELPHI

No. To fulfil the prophecy, this has to be you, not a puppet of you ... you have to be the one to humiliate Cedric, so Imperio just won't do – I'll have to force you by other means.

She takes out her wand. She points it at ALBUS, *who sticks his chin out.*

ALBUS
Do your worst.

DELPHI *looks at him. And then turns her wand on*
SCORPIUS.

DELPHI
I will.

ALBUS
No!

DELPHI
Yes, as I thought – this seems to frighten you more.

SCORPIUS
Albus, whatever she does to me – we can't let her—

DELPHI
Crucio!

SCORPIUS *yells out in pain.*

ALBUS
I will . . .

DELPHI *(laughing)*
What? What on earth do you think you can do? A
wizardwide disappointment? A sore on your family name? A
spare? You want to stop me hurting your only friend? Then
do what you're told.

She looks at ALBUS. *His eyes stay resistant.*

No? Crucio!

ALBUS
Stop! Please.

CRAIG *runs in, full of energy.*

CRAIG BOWKER JR
  Scorpius? Albus? Everyone's looking for you—

ALBUS
  Craig! Get away. Get help!

CRAIG BOWKER JR
  What's happening?

DELPHI
  Avada Kedavra!

  DELPHI *sends a blast of green light across the stage.* CRAIG
  is propelled backwards by it – and is immediately killed.
  There's a silence. A silence that seems to last for a long
  time.

Did you not understand? These are not childish games
we are playing here. You are useful to me, your friends are
not.

  ALBUS *and* SCORPIUS *look at* CRAIG'*s body – their minds in*
  hell.

It took me a long time to discover your weakness, Albus
Potter. I thought it was pride, I thought it was the need to
impress your father, but then I realised your weakness was
the same as your father's – friendship. You will do exactly as
you're told, otherwise Scorpius will die, just like that *spare*
did.

  She looks at them both.

Voldemort will return and the Augurey will sit at his side.
Just as it was prophesied. 'When spares are spared, when
time is turned, when unseen children murder their fathers:
then will the Dark Lord return.'

  She smiles. She pulls SCORPIUS *viciously towards her.*

Cedric is the spare, and Albus—

She pulls ALBUS *viciously towards her.*

—the unseen child who will kill his father by rewriting time and so return the Dark Lord.

The Time-Turner starts rotating. She pulls their hands to it.

Now!

And there is a giant whoosh of light. A smash of noise.
And time stops. And then it turns over, thinks a bit, and begins spooling backwards, slow at first . . .
And then it speeds up.
And then there's a sucking noise. And a bang.

ACT THREE SCENE TWENTY

TRIWIZARD TOURNAMENT, MAZE, 1995

The maze is a spiral of hedges that don't stop moving. DELPHI *walks determinedly through it. Behind her she drags* ALBUS *and* SCORPIUS. *Their arms bound, their legs reluctantly moving.*

LUDO BAGMAN
Ladies and gentlemen, boys and girls, I give you –
the greatest – the fabulous – the one – and the only
TRIWIZARD TOURNAMENT!

> *There's a loud cheer.* DELPHI *turns left.*

If you're from Hogwarts. Give me a cheer.

> *There's a loud cheer.*

If you're from Durmstrang – give me a cheer.

> *There's a loud cheer.*

AND IF YOU'RE FROM BEAUXBATONS GIVE ME A
CHEER.

> *There's a fulsome cheer.*
> DELPHI *and the boys are forced to move as a hedge closes upon them.*

The French finally showing us what they're capable of there. Ladies and gentlemen, I give you – the final of the Triwizard tasks. A maze of mysteries, a disease of uncontrollable darkness, for this maze – it lives. It lives.

> VIKTOR KRUM *passes across the stage, moving through the maze.*

And why risk this living nightmare? Because inside this maze is a Cup – and not just any Cup – yes, the Triwizard trophy stands within this vegetation.

DELPHI
Where is he? Where is Cedric?

> A *hedge almost dissects* ALBUS *and* SCORPIUS.

SCORPIUS
The hedges want to kill us too? This gets better and better.

DELPHI
You will keep up or face the consequences.

LUDO BAGMAN
The perils are plentiful, but the prizes are palpable. Who will fight their way through? Who will fall at the final hurdle? What heroes do we have within our midst? Only time will tell, ladies and gentlemen, only time will tell.

> *They move through the maze,* SCORPIUS *and* ALBUS *being compelled by* DELPHI. *As she moves ahead, the boys have a chance to talk.*

SCORPIUS
Albus, we need to do something.

ALBUS
I know but what? She has snapped our wands, we're bound and she's threatening to kill you.

SCORPIUS
I'm ready to die if it'll stop Voldemort returning.

ALBUS

Are you?

SCORPIUS

You won't have to mourn me for long, she'll kill me and quickly kill you too.

ALBUS (*desperate*)

The flaw in the Time-Turner, the five-minute rule. We do all we can to run down the clock.

SCORPIUS

It won't work.

As another hedge changes direction, DELPHI *pulls* ALBUS *and* SCORPIUS *in after her. They continue through this maze of despair.*

LUDO BAGMAN

Now let me remind you of the current standings! Tied in first place – Mr Cedric Diggory and Mr Harry Potter. In second place – Mr Viktor Krum! And in third place – sacré bleu, Miss Fleur Delacour.

Suddenly, ALBUS *and* SCORPIUS *emerge from behind a maze, they're running.*

ALBUS

Where did she go?

SCORPIUS

Does it matter? Which way do you think?

DELPHI *rises up after them. She's flying, and without a broom.*

DELPHI

You poor creatures.

She throws the boys to the ground.

Thinking you can escape me.

ALBUS (*astonished*)
> You're not – even on a broom.

DELPHI
> Brooms – such unwieldy unnecessary objects. Three
> minutes gone. We have two minutes left. And you will do
> what you're told.

SCORPIUS
> No. We won't.

DELPHI
> You think you can fight me?

SCORPIUS
> No. But we can defy you. If we lay down our lives to do so.

DELPHI
> The prophecy must be fulfilled. We will fulfil it.

SCORPIUS
> Prophecies can be broken.

DELPHI
> You're mistaken child, prophecies are the future.

SCORPIUS
> But if the prophecy is inevitable why are we here trying
> to influence it? Your actions contradict your thoughts –
> you're dragging us through this maze because you believe
> this prophecy needs to be enabled – and by that logic
> prophecies can also be broken – prevented.

DELPHI
> You talk too much, child. Crucio!

> SCORPIUS *is racked with pain.*

ALBUS
> Scorpius!

SCORPIUS
> You wanted a test, Albus – this is it, and we're going to
> pass it.

ALBUS *looks at* SCORPIUS, *finally aware what he has to do. He nods.*

DELPHI

Then you will die.

ALBUS *(full of strength)*

Yes. We will. And we'll do so gladly knowing it's stopped you.

DELPHI *rises up, full of fury.*

DELPHI

We don't have time for this. Cru—

MYSTERIOUS VOICE

Expelliarmus!

Bang. DELPHI's *wand is pulled away from her.* SCORPIUS *looks on in astonishment.*

Brachiabindo!

And DELPHI *is bound.* SCORPIUS *and* ALBUS *then turn as one and stare in astonishment at where the bolt came from: from a young, good-looking lad of seventeen or so,* CEDRIC.

CEDRIC

Come no further.

SCORPIUS

But you're . . .

CEDRIC

Cedric Diggory. I heard screaming, I had to come. Name yourselves, beasts, I can fight you.

ALBUS *wheels around, astonished.*

ALBUS

Cedric?

SCORPIUS
You saved us.

CEDRIC
Are you also a task? An obstacle? Speak. Do I have to defeat you too?

There's a silence.

SCORPIUS
No. You just have to free us. That's the task.

CEDRIC *thinks, trying to work out whether it's a trap, and then waves his wand.*

CEDRIC
Emancipare! Emancipare!

The boys are freed.

And now I can go on? Finish the maze?

The boys look at CEDRIC *– heartbroken.*

ALBUS
I'm afraid you have to finish the maze.

CEDRIC
Then I shall.

CEDRIC *walks confidently away.* ALBUS *looks after him – desperate to say something, unsure what to say.*

ALBUS
Cedric—

CEDRIC *turns towards him.*

Your dad loves you very much.

CEDRIC
What?

Behind them, DELPHI's *body creeps into movement. She crawls along the ground.*

ALBUS

Just thought you should know that.

CEDRIC

Okay. Um. Thank you.

CEDRIC *looks at* ALBUS *a moment more, and then walks on.* DELPHI *pulls out the Time-Turner from within her robes.*

SCORPIUS

Albus.

ALBUS

No. Wait . . .

SCORPIUS

The Time Turner is spinning . . . look at what she's doing . . . she can't leave us behind.

ALBUS *and* SCORPIUS *both scramble to grab part of the Time-Turner.*

And there is a giant whoosh of light. A smash of noise.

And time stops. And then it turns over, thinks a bit, and begins spooling backwards, slow at first . . .

And then it speeds up.

Albus . . .

ALBUS

What have we done?

SCORPIUS

We had to go with the Time-Turner, we had to try to stop her.

DELPHI

Stop me? How do you think you've stopped me? I am done with this. You may have destroyed my chances of

using Cedric to darken the world but maybe you're right
Scorpius – maybe prophecies can be prevented, maybe
prophecies can be broken. What is undoubtedly true is
I'm done with trying to use you annoying, incompetent
creatures for anything. No more wasting precious seconds
on either of you. Time to try something new.

*She crushes the Time-Turner. It explodes into a thousand
pieces.*

DELPHI *ascends again into the air. She laughs in delight as
she sets off, hard away.*

*The boys try to chase her, but they've not the slightest
chance. She flies, they run.*

ALBUS

No ... no ... you can't ...

SCORPIUS *turns back and tries to pick up the Time-Turner
pieces.*

The Time-Turner? It's destroyed?

SCORPIUS

Utterly. We're stuck here. In time. Wherever in time we are.
Whatever it is she's planning to do.

ALBUS

Hogwarts looks the same.

SCORPIUS

Yes. And we can't be seen here. Let's get out of here before
we're spotted.

ALBUS

We need to stop her, Scorpius.

SCORPIUS

I know we do – but how?

ACT THREE   SCENE TWENTY-ONE

ST OSWALD'S HOME FOR OLD WITCHES AND WIZARDS, DELPHI'S ROOM

HARRY, HERMIONE, RON, DRACO *and* GINNY *look around a simple oak-panelled room.*

HARRY
It must have been a Confundus Charm she used on him. Used on them all. She faked being a nurse, she faked being his niece.

HERMIONE
I've just checked in with the Ministry – but there's no record of her. She's a shadow.

DRACO
Specialis Revelio!

Everyone turns to look at DRACO.

Well, it was worth a try, what are you waiting for? We know nothing, so we just have to hope this room reveals something.

GINNY
Where can she have hidden anything? It's quite a spartan room.

RON
> These panels, these panels must conceal something.

DRACO
> Or the bed.

> > DRACO *starts examining the bed,* GINNY *a lamp, as the rest start examining the panels.*

RON *(shouting as he hammers on the walls)*
> What you hiding? What you got?

HERMIONE
> Maybe we should all stop for a moment and have a think about what—

> > GINNY *unscrews a lamp chimney from an oil lamp. There's a breathing-out noise. And then hissing words. They all turn towards it.*

> What was that?

HARRY
> That's – I'm not supposed to be understanding – that's Parseltongue.

HERMIONE
> And what does it say?

HARRY
> How do I ... ? I haven't been able to understand Parseltongue since Voldemort died.

HERMIONE
> And nor has your scar hurt.

> > HARRY *looks at* HERMIONE.

HARRY
> It says 'welcome Augurey'. I think I need to tell it to open ...

DRACO
> Then do it.

HARRY *shuts his eyes. He speaks in Parseltongue.*

The room transforms around them, becoming darker, and more desperate. A writhing mass of painted snakes emerges on all the walls.

And on them, written in fluorescent paint, a prophecy.

What is this?

RON

'When spares are spared, when time is turned, when unseen children murder their fathers: then will the Dark Lord return.'

GINNY

A prophecy. A new prophecy.

HERMIONE

Cedric – Cedric was called a spare.

RON

When time is turned – she has that Time-Turner doesn't she?

Their faces sink.

HERMIONE

She must do.

RON

But why does she need Scorpius or Albus?

HARRY

Because I'm a parent – who hasn't seen his child. Hasn't understood his child.

DRACO

Who is she? To be so obsessed with all this?

GINNY

I think I've got the answer to that.

They all turn to her. She points up . . . their collective faces sink further and fill with fear.

Words are revealed on all the walls of the auditorium –
dangerous words, horrible words.

'I will rebirth the Dark. I will bring my father back.'

RON
No. She can't . . .

HERMIONE
How is it even – possible?

DRACO
Voldemort had a daughter?

They look up terrified. GINNY *takes* HARRY's *hand.*

HARRY
No, no, no. Not that. Anything but that.

We cut to black.

INTERVAL

PART TWO

ACT FOUR

ACT FOUR SCENE ONE

MINISTRY OF MAGIC, GRAND MEETING ROOM

Wizards and witches from all over cram into the grand meeting room.
HERMIONE *walks on to a hastily made stage. She raises her hand for*
silence. Silence falls. She's surprised at the lack of effort it took. She
looks around herself.

HERMIONE

Thank you. I'm so pleased so many of you were able to
make my – second – Extraordinary General Meeting. I've
got some things to say – I ask that we deal with questions –
and there will be a lot of questions – after I speak.

As many of you know, a body has been found at Hogwarts.
His name was Craig Bowker. He was a good boy. We have
no firm information who was responsible for the act but
yesterday we searched St Oswald's. A room there revealed
two things: one, a prophecy that promised . . . the return
of darkness – two, written on the ceiling, a proclamation –
that the Dark Lord had a – that Voldemort had a child.

The news reverberates around the room.

We don't know the full details. We're only just
investigating – questioning those with a Death Eater
connection . . . and as yet no record has been found either

of the child or of the prophecy, but, it does look like there's some truth to it. This child was kept hidden from the wizarding world, and now she's – well now she's—

PROFESSOR McGONAGALL
She? A daughter? He had a daughter?

HERMIONE
Yes. A daughter.

PROFESSOR McGONAGALL
And is she now in custody?

HARRY
Professor, she did ask for no questions.

HERMIONE
It's fine, Harry. No, Professor, that's where this gets worse. I'm afraid we've no means of taking her into custody. Or indeed, stopping her doing anything. She's out of our reach.

PROFESSOR McGONAGALL
We can't – look for her?

HERMIONE
We have good reason to believe she's hidden herself – in time.

PROFESSOR McGONAGALL
Of all the reckless stupid things, you've kept the Time-Turner even now?

HERMIONE
Professor, I assure you—

PROFESSOR McGONAGALL
Shame on you, Hermione Granger!

HERMIONE *flinches in the face of the anger.*

HARRY
No, she doesn't deserve that. You have a right to be angry. You all do. But this is not all Hermione's fault. We don't

know how the witch got hold of the Time-Turner. Whether
my son gave it to her.

GINNY

Whether our son gave it her. Or whether it was stolen from
him.

> GINNY *joins* HARRY *on the stage.*

PROFESSOR McGONAGALL

Your solidarity is admirable, but it doesn't make your
negligence negligible.

DRACO

Then it's a negligence I too should face.

> DRACO *walks up to the stage and stands beside* GINNY.
> *This is almost a Spartacus moment. There are gasps.*

Hermione and Harry have done nothing wrong but try and
protect us all. If they're guilty, then I am too.

> HERMIONE *looks across at her cohort – moved.* RON *joins*
> *them on the stage.*

RON

Just to say – I didn't know about much of it so can't take
responsibility – and I'm pretty sure my kids had nothing
to do with it – but if this lot are standing up here, then so
am I.

GINNY

No one can know where they are – whether they're
together or apart. I trust that our sons will be doing all they
can to stop her but . . .

HERMIONE

We haven't given up. We've gone to the giants. The trolls.
Everyone we can find. The Aurors are out flying, searching,
talking to those who know secrets, following those who
won't reveal secrets.

HARRY

But there is one truth we can't escape: that somewhere in our past a witch is trying to rewrite everything we ever knew – and all we can do is wait – wait for the moment she either succeeds or fails.

PROFESSOR McGONAGALL

And if she succeeds?

HARRY

Then – just like that – most of the people in this room will be gone, we'll no longer exist and Voldemort will rule again.

ACT FOUR   SCENE TWO

SCOTTISH HIGHLANDS, AVIEMORE TRAIN STATION, 1981

ALBUS *and* SCORPIUS *are looking at a* STATION MASTER, *apprehensively.*

ALBUS

One of us should talk to him, don't you think?

SCORPIUS

Hello, Mr Station Master. Mr Muggle. Question: did you
see a flying witch passing here? And by the way, what year
is it? We just ran away from Hogwarts because we were
frightened of upsetting things, but this is okay?

ALBUS

You know what annoys me most of all? Dad will think we
did it deliberately.

SCORPIUS

Albus. Really? I mean, really really? We're – trapped – lost –
in time – probably permanently – and you're worrying what
your dad might think about it? I will never understand the
two of you.

ALBUS

There's a lot to understand. Dad's pretty complicated.

SCORPIUS

And you're not? Not to question your taste in women but
you fancied . . . well . . .

267

They both know who he's talking about.

ALBUS
I did, didn't I? I mean what she did to Craig . . .

SCORPIUS
Let's not think about that. Let's focus on the fact that we have no wands, no brooms, no means of returning to our time, all we have is our wits and – no, that's all, our wits – and we have to stop her.

STATION MASTER *(in very strong Scots)*
Ye ken th' Auld Reekie train is running late, boys?

SCORPIUS
Sorry?

STATION MASTER
If you're waiting oan th' Auld Reekie train, you'll need tae ken it's running late. Train wirks oan th' line. It's a' oan th' amended time buird.

He looks at them, they look back bewildered. He frowns and hands them an amended timetable. He points to the right bit of it.

Late.

ALBUS takes it and examines it. His face changes as he takes in enormous information. SCORPIUS just stares at the Station Master.

ALBUS
I know where she is.

SCORPIUS
You understood that?

ALBUS
Look at the date. On the timetable.

SCORPIUS leans in and reads.

SCORPIUS

The thirtieth of October 1981. Day before Hallows' Eve, thirty-nine years ago. But – why is she? Oh.

SCORPIUS's *face falls as he realises.*

ALBUS

The death of my grandparents. The attack on my dad as a baby ... the moment when Voldemort's curse rebounded on himself. She's not trying to bring about her prophecy – she's trying to prevent the big one.

SCORPIUS

The big one?

ALBUS

'The one with the power to vanquish the Dark Lord approaches ...

SCORPIUS *joins in.*

SCORPIUS *and* ALBUS

'... born to those who have thrice defied him, born as the seventh month dies ...'

SCORPIUS's *face falls with every word.*

SCORPIUS

It's my fault. I told her that prophecies can be broken – I told her the whole logic of prophecies is questionable—

ALBUS

In twenty-four hours' time Voldemort curses himself trying to kill the baby Harry Potter. Delphi is trying to prevent that curse. She's going to kill Harry herself. We need to get to Godric's Hollow. Now.

ACT FOUR SCENE THREE

GODRIC'S HOLLOW, 1981

ALBUS *and* SCORPIUS *walk through the centre of Godric's Hollow and it's a bustling, beautiful little village.*

SCORPIUS
Well, there's no visible signs of attack that I can see . . .

ALBUS
This is Godric's Hollow?

SCORPIUS
Your dad's never taken you?

ALBUS
No, he tried to a few times but I refused.

SCORPIUS
Well there's no time for a tour – we have a murderous witch to save the world from – but regard . . . the church, St Jerome's . . .

As he indicates a church becomes visible.

ALBUS
It's magnificent.

SCORPIUS

And St Jerome's graveyard is supposedly magnificently haunted (*he points in another direction*), and that's where the statue of Harry and his parents will be—

ALBUS

My dad has a statue?

SCORPIUS

Oh. Not yet. But he will. Hopefully. And this – this house is where Bathilda Bagshot lived, lives . . .

ALBUS

The Bathilda Bagshot? *A History of Magic* Bathilda Bagshot?

SCORPIUS

The very same. Oh my, that's her. Wow. Squeak. My geekness is a-quivering.

ALBUS

Scorpius!

SCORPIUS

And here it is—

ALBUS

The home of James, Lily and Harry Potter . . .

A young, attractive couple leave a house with a baby in a pushchair. ALBUS moves towards them, SCORPIUS pulls him back.

SCORPIUS

They can't see you, Albus, it might damage time, and we're not doing that – not this time.

ALBUS

But this means, she hasn't . . . we've made it . . . she hasn't . . .

SCORPIUS

So what do we do now? Get ready to fight her? Because she's pretty . . . fierce.

ALBUS

Yes. We haven't really thought this one through have we? What do we do now? How do we protect my dad?

ACT FOUR SCENE FOUR

MINISTRY OF MAGIC, HARRY'S OFFICE

HARRY *is hurriedly going through paperwork.*

DUMBLEDORE
Good evening, Harry.

> *Beat.* HARRY *looks up at the portrait of* DUMBLEDORE, *his face passive.*

HARRY
Professor Dumbledore. In my office, I'm honoured. I must be where the action is, tonight?

DUMBLEDORE
What are you doing?

HARRY
Going through papers, seeing if I've missed anything I shouldn't have. Marshalling forces to fight in the limited way we can fight. Knowing that the battle is being raged far away from us. What else can I do?

> *Pause.* DUMBLEDORE *says nothing.*

Where have you been, Dumbledore?

DUMBLEDORE
I'm here now.

HARRY

Here just as the battle is lost. Or are you denying that Voldemort is going to return?

DUMBLEDORE

It is – possible.

HARRY

Go. Leave. I don't want you here, I don't need you. You were absent every time it really counted. I fought him three times without you. I'll face him again, if needs be – alone.

DUMBLEDORE

Harry, don't you think I wanted to fight him on your behalf? I would have spared you if I could—

HARRY

Love blinds us? Do you even know what that means? Do you even know how bad that advice was? My son is – my son is fighting battles for us just as I had to for you. And I have proved as bad a father to him as you were to me. Leaving him in places he felt unloved – growing in him resentments he'll take years to understand—

DUMBLEDORE

If you're referring to Privet Drive then—

HARRY

Years – years I spent there alone, without knowing what I was, or why I was there, without knowing that anybody cared!

DUMBLEDORE

I – did not wish to become attached to you—

HARRY

Protecting yourself, even then!

DUMBLEDORE

No. I was protecting you. I did not want to hurt you . . .

> **DUMBLEDORE** *attempts to reach out of the portrait, but he can't. He begins to cry but tries to hide it.*

But I had to meet you in the end . . . eleven years old, and you were so brave. So good. You walked uncomplainingly along the path that had been laid at your feet. Of course I loved you . . . and I knew that it would happen all over again . . . that where I loved, I would cause irreparable damage . . . I am no fit person to love . . . I have never loved without causing harm . . .

Beat.

HARRY
You would have hurt me less if you had told me this, then.

DUMBLEDORE *(openly weeping now)*
I was blind. That is what love does. I couldn't see that you needed to hear that this closed-up, tricky, dangerous old man . . . loved you . . .

A pause. The two men are overcome with emotion.

HARRY
It isn't true that I never complained.

DUMBLEDORE
Harry, there is never a perfect answer in this messy, emotional world. Perfection is beyond the reach of humankind, beyond the reach of magic. In every shining moment of happiness is that drop of poison: the knowledge that pain will come again. Be honest to those you love, show your pain. To suffer is as human as to breathe.

HARRY
You said that to me once before.

DUMBLEDORE
It is all I have to offer you tonight.

He begins to walk away.

HARRY
Don't go!

DUMBLEDORE

Those that we love never truly leave us, Harry. There are things that death cannot touch. Paint … and memory … and love.

HARRY

I loved you too, Dumbledore.

DUMBLEDORE

I know.

He is gone. And HARRY *is alone.* DRACO *enters.*

DRACO

Did you know that in this other reality – the reality Scorpius saw into – I was Head of Magical Law Enforcement? Maybe this room will be mine soon enough. Are you okay?

HARRY *is consumed in his grief.*

HARRY

Come in – I'll give you the tour.

DRACO *walks hesitantly inside the room. He looks around distastefully.*

DRACO

The thing is though – never really fancied being a Ministry man. Even as a child. My dad – it's all he ever wanted – me, no.

HARRY

What did you want to do?

DRACO

Quidditch. But I wasn't good enough. Mainly I wanted to be happy.

HARRY *nods.* DRACO *looks at him a second more.*

Sorry, I'm not very good at small talk, do you mind if we skip on to the serious business?

HARRY

Of course. What – serious – business?

Beat.

DRACO

Do you think Theodore Nott had the only Time-Turner?

HARRY

What?

DRACO

The Time-Turner the Ministry seized was a prototype.
Made of inexpensive metal. It does the job, sure. But only
being able to go back in time for five minutes – that's a
serious flaw – it isn't something you'd sell to true collectors
of Dark Magic.

HARRY *realises what* DRACO *is saying.*

HARRY

He was working for you?

DRACO

No. My father. He liked owning things that no one else
had. The Ministry's Time-Turners – thanks to Croaker –
were always a little vanilla for him. He wanted the ability
to go back further than an hour, he wanted the ability to
travel back years. He'd never have used it, secretly I think
he preferred a world without Voldemort. But yes, the Time-
Turner was built for him.

HARRY

And did you keep it?

DRACO *reveals the Time-Turner.*

DRACO

No five-minute problem, and it gleams like gold, just the
way the Malfoys like it. You're smiling.

HARRY

Hermione Granger. It was the reason she kept the first, the fear that there might be a second. Hanging on to this, you could have been sent to Azkaban.

DRACO

Consider the alternative – consider if people had known that I had the ability to travel in time. Consider the rumour that would have been given increased – credence.

HARRY *looks at* DRACO, *understanding him perfectly.*

HARRY

Scorpius.

DRACO

We were capable of having children, but Astoria was frail. A blood malediction, a serious one. An ancestor was cursed ... it showed up in her. You know how these things can resurface after generations ...

HARRY

I'm sorry, Draco.

DRACO

I didn't want to risk her health, I said it didn't matter whether the Malfoy line died with me – whatever my father said. But Astoria – she didn't want a baby for the Malfoy name, for pure blood or glory, but for us. Our child, Scorpius was born ... it was the best day of both our lives, although it weakened Astoria considerably. We hid ourselves away, the three of us. I wanted to conserve her strength ... and so the rumours started.

HARRY

I can't imagine what that was like.

DRACO

Astoria always knew that she was not destined for old age. She wanted me to have somebody when she left, because ... it is exceptionally lonely, being Draco Malfoy.

I will always be suspected. There is no escaping the past. I
never realised, though, that by hiding him away from this
gossiping, judgemental world, I ensured that my son would
emerge shrouded in worse suspicion than I ever endured.

HARRY

Love blinds. We have both tried to give our sons not what
they needed, but what we needed. We've been so busy
trying to rewrite our own pasts, we've blighted their present.

DRACO

Which is why you need this. I have been holding on to it,
barely resisting using it, even though I would sell my soul
for another minute with Astoria . . .

HARRY

Oh, Draco . . . we can't. We can't use it.

> DRACO *looks up at* HARRY, *and for the first time – at the
> bottom of this dreadful pit – they look at each other as
> friends.*

DRACO

We have to find them – if it takes centuries, we must find
our sons . . .

HARRY

We have no idea where they are or when they are.
Searching in time when you've no idea where in time to
search, that's a fool's errand. No, love won't do it and nor
will a Time-Turner, I'm afraid. It's up to our sons now –
they're the only ones who can save us.

ACT FOUR SCENE FIVE

GODRIC'S HOLLOW, OUTSIDE JAMES AND LILY POTTER'S HOUSE, 1981

ALBUS

We tell my granddad and grandma?

SCORPIUS

That they'll never get to see their son grow up?

ALBUS

She's strong enough – I know she is – you saw her.

SCORPIUS

She looked wonderful, Albus. And if I were you I'd be desperate to talk to her. But she needs to be able to beg Voldemort for Harry's life, she needs to think he might die, and you're the worst spoiler in the world that didn't turn out to be true . . .

ALBUS

Dumbledore. Dumbledore's alive. We get Dumbledore involved. We do what you did with Snape—

SCORPIUS

Can we risk him knowing your dad survives? That he has kids?

ALBUS

He's Dumbledore! He can cope with anything!

SCORPIUS

Albus, there have been about a hundred books written
on what Dumbledore knew, how he knew it or why he did
what he did. But what's undoubtedly true – what he did –
he needs to do – and I'm not going to risk messing with
it. I was able to ask for help because I was in an alternate
reality. We aren't. We're in the past. We can't fix time only
to create more problems – if our adventures have taught us
anything, they've taught us that. The dangers of talking to
anyone – infecting time – are too great.

ALBUS

So we need to – talk to the future. We need to send Dad a
message.

SCORPIUS

But we don't have an owl that can fly through time. And he
doesn't have a Time-Turner.

ALBUS

We get a message to Dad. He'll find a way to get back here.
Even if he has to build a Time-Turner himself.

SCORPIUS

We send a memory – like a Pensieve – stand over him and
send a message, hope he reaches for the memory at exactly
the right moment. I mean, it's unlikely, but ... stand over
the baby – and just repeatedly shout HELP. HELP. HELP. I
mean, it might traumatise the baby slightly.

ALBUS

Only slightly.

SCORPIUS

A bit of trauma now is nothing compared to what's
happening ... and maybe when he then thinks – later – he
might remember the faces of us as we – shouted—

ALBUS

Help.

SCORPIUS *looks at* ALBUS.

SCORPIUS
You're right. It's a terrible idea.

ALBUS
It's one of your worst ideas ever.

SCORPIUS
Got it! We deliver it ourselves – we wait forty years – we
deliver it—

ALBUS
Not a chance – once Delphi has set time the way she wants
she'll send armies to try and find us – kill us—

SCORPIUS
So we hide in a hole?

ALBUS
As pleasurable as it will be to hide in a hole with you for
the next forty years . . . they'll find us. And we'll die and
time will be stuck in the wrong position. No. We need
something we can control, something we know he'll get at
exactly the right time. We need a . . .

SCORPIUS
There's nothing. Still, if I had to choose a companion to be
at the return of eternal darkness with, I'd choose you.

ALBUS
No offence, but I'd choose someone massive and really good
at magic.

LILY *exits the house with* BABY HARRY *in a pram, she
carefully puts a blanket on him.*

His blanket. She's wrapping him in his blanket.

SCORPIUS
Well, it is a moderately cold day.

ALBUS
He always said – it's the only thing he had from her. Look

at the love with which she's put it on him – I think he'd like
to know about that – I wish I could tell him.

SCORPIUS

And I wish I could tell my dad – well, I'm not sure what.
I think I'd like to tell him that I'm occasionally capable of
more bravery than he might think I am.

ALBUS *has a thought.*

ALBUS

Scorpius – my dad still has that blanket.

SCORPIUS

That won't work. If we write a message on it now, even
really small, he'll read it too soon. Time will be spoilt.

ALBUS

What do you know about love potions? What's the
ingredient they all contain?

SCORPIUS

Amongst other things, Pearl Dust.

ALBUS

Pearl Dust is a relatively rare ingredient isn't it?

SCORPIUS

Mainly because it's pretty expensive. What's this about,
Albus?

ALBUS

Dad and I had a fight on the day before I went to school.

SCORPIUS

This I am aware of. I believe it kind of got us into this mess.

ALBUS

I threw the blanket across the room. It collided with the
love potion that Uncle Ron gave me as a joke.

SCORPIUS

He's a funny guy.

ALBUS

The potion spilt and the blanket was covered in it and I
happen to know for a fact Mum hasn't let Dad touch that
room since I left it.

SCORPIUS

So?

ALBUS

So it's coming up to Hallows' Eve in their time as well as
ours – and he told me he always finds that blanket, he
needs to be with it on Hallows' Eve – it was the last thing
his mum gave him – so he will look for it and when he finds
it . . .

SCORPIUS

No. Still not getting you.

ALBUS

What reacts with Pearl Dust?

SCORPIUS

Well, it is said that if Tincture of Demiguise and Pearl Dust
meet . . . they burn.

ALBUS

And is Tincture of (*he's unsure how to say the word*)
Demiguise visible to the naked eye?

SCORPIUS

No.

ALBUS

So if we were to get that blanket and write on it in
Tincture of Demiguise then . . .

SCORPIUS (*eureka*)

Nothing would react to it until it came into contact
with the love potion. In your room. In the present. By
Dumbledore, I love it.

ALBUS

We just need to work out where to find some . . .
Demiguises.

SCORPIUS

You know, rumour has it Bathilda Bagshot never saw the
point in witches and wizards locking their doors.

The door swings open.

Rumour was right. Time to steal some wands and get
potioning.

———

ACT FOUR SCENE SIX

HARRY AND GINNY POTTER'S HOUSE, ALBUS'S ROOM

HARRY *is sitting on* ALBUS's *bed.* GINNY *enters, she looks at him.*

GINNY
Surprised to find you here.

HARRY
Don't worry, I haven't touched anything. Your shrine is preserved. (*He winces.*) Sorry. Bad choice of words.

GINNY *says nothing.* HARRY *looks up at her.*

You know I've had some pretty terrible Hallows' Eves – but this is undoubtedly at least the – second worst.

GINNY
I was wrong – to blame you – I always accuse you of jumping to things and it was me who – Albus went missing and I assumed it was your fault. I'm sorry I did that.

HARRY
You don't think this is my fault?

GINNY
Harry, he was kidnapped by a powerful Dark witch, how can that be your fault?

HARRY
I chased him away. I chased him to her.

286

GINNY

Can we not treat this as if the battle is already lost?

GINNY nods. HARRY starts to cry.

HARRY

I'm sorry Gin—

GINNY

Are you not listening to me? I'm sorry too.

HARRY

I shouldn't have survived – it was my destiny to die – even Dumbledore thought so – and yet I lived. I beat Voldemort. All these people – all these people – my parents, Fred, the Fallen Fifty – and it's me that gets to live? How is that? All this damage – and it's my fault.

GINNY

They were killed by Voldemort.

HARRY

But if I'd stopped him sooner? All that blood on my hands. And now our son has been taken too—

GINNY

He's not dead. Do you hear me Harry? He's not dead.

She takes HARRY in her arms. There is a big pause filled with pure unhappiness.

HARRY

The Boy Who Lived. How many people have to die for the Boy Who Lived?

HARRY sways a moment, unsure. Then he notices the blanket. He walks towards it.

This blanket is all I have you know . . . of that Hallows' Eve. This is all I have to remember them. And whilst—

He picks up the blanket. He discovers it has holes in it. He looks at it, dismayed.

287

This has got holes in it. Ron's idiotic love potion has
burnt through it, right through it. Look at this. It's ruined.
Ruined.

*He opens up the blanket. He sees writing burnt through
it. He's surprised.*

What?

GINNY
Harry, it has – something – written—

On another part of the stage ALBUS *and* SCORPIUS *appear.*

ALBUS
'Dad . . .'

SCORPIUS
We're starting with 'Dad'?

ALBUS
So he'll know it's from me.

SCORPIUS
Harry is his name. We should start with 'Harry'.

ALBUS *(firm)*
We're starting with 'Dad'.

HARRY
'Dad', does it say 'Dad'? It's not that distinct . . .

SCORPIUS
'Dad, HELP.'

GINNY
'Hello'? Does that say 'Hello'? And then . . . 'Good' . . .

HARRY
'Dad Hello Good Hello'? No. This is . . . a strange joke.

ALBUS
'Dad. Help. Godric's Hollow.'

GINNY
Give me that. My eyesight is better than yours. Yes. 'Dad

Hello Good' – that's not 'Hello' again – that's 'Hallow' or 'Hollow'? And then some numbers – these are clearer – '3 . . . 1 . . . 1 . . . 0 . . . 8 . . . 1'. Is this one of those Muggle telephone numbers? Or a grid reference or a . . .

> HARRY *looks up, several thoughts smashing through his brain at once.*

HARRY

No. It's a date. 31 October 1981. The date my parents were killed.

> GINNY *looks at* HARRY, *and then back at the blanket.*

GINNY

That doesn't say 'Hello'. It says 'Help'.

HARRY

'Dad. Help. Godric's Hollow. 31/10/81.' It's a message. Clever boy left me a message.

> HARRY *kisses* GINNY *hard.*

GINNY

Albus wrote this?

HARRY

And he's told me where they are and when they are, and now we know where she is, we know where we can fight her.

> *He kisses her hard again.*

GINNY

We haven't got them back again yet.

HARRY

I'll send an owl to Hermione. You send one to Draco. Tell them to meet us at Godric's Hollow with the Time-Turner.

GINNY

And it is 'us', okay? Don't even think about going back
without me, Harry.

HARRY

Of course you're coming. We have a chance Ginny, and by
Dumbledore – that's all that we need – a chance.

ACT FOUR   SCENE SEVEN

GODRIC'S HOLLOW

RON, HERMIONE, DRACO, HARRY *and* GINNY *walk through a present-day Godric's Hollow. A busy market town (it's expanded over the years).*

HERMIONE

Godric's Hollow. It must be twenty years . . .

GINNY

Is it just me or are there more Muggles about?

HERMIONE

It's become quite popular as a weekend break.

DRACO

I can see why – look at the thatched roofs. And is that a farmers' market?

> HERMIONE *approaches* HARRY – *who is looking around himself, overwhelmed by all he is seeing.*

HERMIONE

You remember when we were last here? This feels just like old times.

RON

Old times with a few unwelcome ponytails added to the mix.

> DRACO *knows a barb when he hears one.*

DRACO

> Can I just say . . .

RON

> Malfoy, you may be all chummy chummy with Harry, and
> you may have produced a relatively nice child, but you've
> said some very unfair things to and about my wife . . .

HERMIONE

> And your wife doesn't need you fighting her battles for her.

> HERMIONE *looks witheringly at* RON. RON *takes the hit.*

RON

> Fine. But if you say one thing about her or me . . .

DRACO

> You'll do what, Weasley?

HERMIONE

> He'll hug you. Because we're all on the same team, aren't we
> Ron?

RON *(hesitating in the face of her unwavering gaze)*
> Fine. I, um, I think you've got really nice hair. Draco.

HERMIONE

> Thank you, husband. Now this seems a good spot. Let's do
> this . . .

> > DRACO *takes out the Time-Turner – it begins spinning
> > wildly as the others take their places around it.*
> > *And there is a giant whoosh of light. A smash of noise.*
> > *And time stops. And then it turns over, thinks a bit, and
> > begins spooling backwards, slow at first . . .*
> > *And then it speeds up.*
> > *They look around themselves.*

RON

> So? Has it worked?

ACT FOUR   SCENE EIGHT

GODRIC'S HOLLOW, A SHED, 1981

ALBUS *looks up amazed to see* GINNY *and then* HARRY, *and then he takes in the rest of the happy band (*RON, DRACO *and* HERMIONE*).*

ALBUS
MUM?

HARRY
Albus Severus Potter. Are we pleased to see you.

> ALBUS *runs and throws himself into* GINNY'S *arms.* GINNY *receives him, delighted.*

ALBUS
You got our note . . . ?

GINNY
We got your note.

> SCORPIUS *trots up to his dad.*

DRACO
We can hug too if you like . . .

> SCORPIUS *looks at his dad, unsure for a moment. And then they sort of half-hug in a very awkward way.* DRACO *smiles.*

RON

Now, where's this Delphi?

SCORPIUS

You know about Delphi?

ALBUS

She's here – she's trying to kill you we think. Before
Voldemort curses himself. She's going to kill you and so
break the prophecy and . . .

HERMIONE

Yes, we thought that might be it too. Do you know where
specifically she is now?

SCORPIUS

She's disappeared. How did you – how did you without the
Time-Turner . . .

HARRY *(interrupting)*

That's a long and complicated story, Scorpius. And we don't
have time for it.

DRACO *smiles at* HARRY *gratefully.*

HERMIONE

Harry's right. Time is of the essence. We need to get people
into position. Now, Godric's Hollow is not a large place,
but she could be coming from any direction. So we need
somewhere that gives us good views of the town – that
allows for multiple and clear observation points – and that
will, most importantly, keep us hidden because we cannot
risk being seen.

They all frown, thinking.

I'd say St Jerome's Church ticks all those boxes wouldn't
you?

ACT FOUR   SCENE NINE

GODRIC'S HOLLOW, CHURCH, SANCTUARY, 1981

ALBUS *is sleeping in a pew.* GINNY *watches him carefully.* HARRY *is looking out the opposite window.*

HARRY

No. Nothing. Why isn't she here?

GINNY

We're together, your mum and dad are alive, we can turn time Harry, we can't speed it up. She'll come when she's ready and we'll be ready for her.

She looks at ALBUS's *sleeping form.*

Or some of us will be.

HARRY

Poor kid thought he had to save the world.

GINNY

Poor kid has saved the world. That blanket was masterful. I mean, he also almost destroyed the world, but probably best not to focus on that bit.

HARRY

You think he's okay?

GINNY

He's getting there, it just might take him a bit of time – and you a bit of time too.

HARRY *smiles. She looks back at* ALBUS. *He does too.*

You know, after I'd opened the Chamber of Secrets – after Voldemort had bewitched me with that terrible diary and I'd almost destroyed everything—

HARRY

I remember.

GINNY

After I came out of hospital – everyone ignored me, shut me out – other than, that is, the boy who had everything – who came across the Gryffindor common room and challenged me to a game of Exploding Snap. People think they know all there is to know about you, but the best bits of you are – have always been – heroic in really quiet ways. My point is – after this is over, just remember if you could – that sometimes people – but particularly children – just want someone to play Exploding Snap with.

HARRY

You think that's what we're missing – Exploding Snap?

GINNY

No. But the love I felt from you that day – I'm not sure Albus feels that.

HARRY

I'd do anything for him.

GINNY

Harry, you'd do anything for anybody. You were pretty happy to sacrifice yourself for the world. He needs to feel specific love. It'll make him stronger, and you stronger too.

HARRY

You know, it wasn't until we thought Albus had gone that I truly understood what my mother was able to do for me. A counter-charm so powerful that it was able to repel the spell of death.

GINNY

And the only spell Voldemort couldn't understand – love.

HARRY

I do love him specifically, Ginny.

GINNY

I know, but he needs to feel it.

HARRY

I'm lucky to have you aren't I?

GINNY

Extremely. And I'd be delighted to discuss just how lucky at another time. But for now – let's focus on stopping Delphi.

HARRY

We are running out of time.

A thought occurs to GINNY.

GINNY

Unless – Harry, has anyone thought – why has she picked now? Today?

HARRY

Because this is the day that everything changed . . .

GINNY

Right now you're over a year old, am I right?

HARRY

A year and three months.

GINNY

That's a year and three months she could have killed you in. Even now, she's been in Godric's Hollow for twenty-four hours. What's she waiting for?

HARRY

I'm still not entirely following—

GINNY

What if she's not waiting for you – she's waiting for him . . . to stop him?

HARRY

What?

GINNY

Delphi's picked tonight because he's here – because her father is coming. She wants to meet him. Be with him, the father she loves. Voldemort's problems started when he attacked you. If he hadn't done that . . .

HARRY

He'd have only got more powerful – the darkness would only have got darker.

GINNY

The best way to break the prophecy is not to kill Harry Potter, it's to stop Voldemort doing anything at all.

ACT FOUR   SCENE TEN

GODRIC'S HOLLOW, CHURCH, 1981

The group are gathered and full of confusion.

RON
So let me get this right – we're fighting to protect Voldemort?

ALBUS
Voldemort killing my grandparents. Voldemort trying to kill my dad?

HERMIONE
Of course, Ginny. Delphi's not trying to kill Harry – she's stopping Voldemort trying to kill Harry. Brilliant.

DRACO
So – we just wait? Until Voldemort turns up?

ALBUS
Does she know when he does turn up? Hasn't she come here twenty-four hours early because she isn't sure when he'll arrive and in what direction? The history books – correct me if I'm wrong, Scorpius – show nothing about when and how he arrived in Godric's Hollow?

SCORPIUS *and* **HERMIONE**
You're not wrong.

RON

Blimey! There are two of them!

DRACO

So how can we use this to our advantage?

ALBUS

Do you know what I'm really good at?

HARRY

There's plenty you're good at, Albus.

ALBUS

Polyjuicing. And I think Bathilda Bagshot may have all the ingredients for Polyjuice in her basement. We can Polyjuice into Voldemort and bring her to us.

RON

To use Polyjuice you need a bit of someone. We don't have a bit of Voldemort.

HERMIONE

But I like the concept, a pretend mouse for her cat.

HARRY

How close can we get through transfiguration?

HERMIONE

We know what he looks like. We've got some excellent wizards and witches here.

GINNY

You want to transfigure into Voldemort?

ALBUS

It's the only way.

HERMIONE

It is, isn't it?

RON *steps forward bravely.*

RON

Then I would like to – I think I should be him. I mean, it won't be – exactly nice being Voldemort – but without

wishing to blow my own trumpet – I am probably the most
chilled out of all of us and . . . so maybe transfiguring into
him – into the Dark Lord will do less damage to me than –
any of you more – intense – people.

HARRY *steps away, introspective.*

HERMIONE
Who are you calling intense?

DRACO
I'd also like to volunteer. I think being Voldemort requires
precision . . . no offence, Ron . . . and a knowledge of Dark
Magic, and—

HERMIONE
And I'd like to volunteer, too. As Minister for Magic I think
it's my responsibility and right.

SCORPIUS
Maybe we should draw lots—

DRACO
You're not volunteering, Scorpius.

ALBUS
Actually—

GINNY
No, no way. I think you're all mad. I know what that voice
is like inside your head. I won't have it in mine again—

HARRY
And anyway – it has to be me.

Everyone turns to HARRY.

DRACO
What?

HARRY
For this plan to work she has to believe it's him, without
hesitation. She'll use Parseltongue – and I *knew* there was
a reason why I still have that ability. But more than that,

I – know what it is to feel – like him. I know what it is to *be* him. It has to be me.

RON

Rubbish. Beautifully put, but beautiful rubbish. No way are you going to—

HERMIONE

I'm afraid you're right, my old friend.

RON

Hermione, you're wrong, Voldemort is not something to be – Harry should not—

GINNY

And I hate to agree with my brother, but . . .

RON

He could get stuck – as Voldemort – forever.

HERMIONE

So could any of us. Your concerns are valid but . . .

HARRY

Hang on, Hermione. Gin.

> GINNY *and* HARRY *make eye contact.*

I won't do it if you don't want me to. But it feels like the only way to me. Am I wrong?

> GINNY *thinks a moment and then softly nods.* HARRY's
> *face hardens.*

GINNY

You're right.

HARRY

Then let's do this.

DRACO

Don't we need to discuss the route you're taking – the—

HARRY

She's watching for him. She'll come to me.

DRACO

And then what? When she's with you? May I remind you this is a very powerful witch.

RON

Easy. He gets her in here. We zap her together.

DRACO

'Zap her'?

HERMIONE *looks around the room.*

HERMIONE

We'll hide behind these doors. If you can get her to this point Harry (*she indicates the point where the light from the church's Rose Window hits the floor*), then we come out and make sure she has no chance to escape.

RON (*with a look to* DRACO)
And then we'll *zap* her.

HERMIONE

Harry, last chance, are you sure you can do this?

HARRY

Yes, I can do this.

DRACO

No, there's too many what ifs – too many things that can go wrong – the transfiguration could not hold, she could see through it – if she escapes us now there's no telling the damage she can do – we need time to properly plan to—

ALBUS

Draco, trust my dad. He won't let us down.

HARRY *looks at* ALBUS – *moved.*

HERMIONE

Wands.

Everyone withdraws their wands. HARRY *clasps his.*
There's a light that builds – that overwhelms.

The transfiguration is slow and monstrous.

And the form of VOLDEMORT *emerges from* HARRY. *And it's horrendous. He turns. He looks around his friends and family. They look back – aghast.*

RON
Bloody hell.

HARRY/VOLDEMORT
It worked, then?

GINNY (*gravely*)
Yes. It worked.

ACT FOUR   SCENE ELEVEN

GODRIC'S HOLLOW, CHURCH, 1981

RON, HERMIONE, DRACO, SCORPIUS *and* ALBUS *stand at the window, looking out.* GINNY *can't look. She sits further back.*

ALBUS *notices his mum sitting apart. He walks over to her.*

ALBUS

It's going to be okay, you know that, Mum?

GINNY

I know it is. Or I hope I do. I just – don't want to see him like that. The man I love shrouded in the man I hate.

ALBUS *sits beside his mum.*

ALBUS

I liked her, Mum. You know that? I really liked her. Delphi. And she was – Voldemort's daughter?

GINNY

That's what they're good at Albus – catching innocents in their web.

ALBUS

This is all my fault.

GINNY *takes* ALBUS *in her arms.*

GINNY

How funny. Your dad seems to think it's all his. Strange pair, you are.

SCORPIUS

That's her. That's her. She's seen him.

HERMIONE

Positions. Everybody. And remember, don't come out until he's got her in the light. We've one shot at this, we don't want to mess it up.

They all move fast.

DRACO

Hermione Granger, I'm being bossed around by Hermione Granger. (*She turns towards him, he smiles.*) And I'm mildly enjoying it.

SCORPIUS

Dad . . .

They scatter. They hide behind two major doors.

HARRY/VOLDEMORT *re-enters the church. He walks a few paces and then he turns.*

HARRY/VOLDEMORT

Whichever witch or wizard is following me, I assure you, you will regret it.

DELPHI *emerges behind him. She is compelled to him. This is her father and this is the moment she's waited for her entire life.*

DELPHI

Lord Voldemort. It is me. I am following you.

HARRY/VOLDEMORT

I do not know you. Leave me.

She breathes deeply.

DELPHI
  I am your daughter.

HARRY/VOLDEMORT
  If you were my daughter, I'd know of you.

  DELPHI *looks at him imploringly.*

DELPHI
  I am from the future. The child of Bellatrix Lestrange
  and you. I was born in Malfoy Manor before the Battle of
  Hogwarts. A battle you are going to lose. I have come to
  save you.

  HARRY/VOLDEMORT *turns. She meets his eyes.*

  It was Rodolphus Lestrange, Bellatrix's loyal husband, who
  on return from Azkaban told me who I was and revealed
  the prophecy he thought I was destined to fulfil. I am your
  daughter, sir.

HARRY/VOLDEMORT
  I am familiar with Bellatrix and there are certain
  similarities in your face – though you haven't inherited the
  best of her. But without proof . . .

  DELPHI *speaks intently in Parseltongue.*

  HARRY/VOLDEMORT *laughs viciously.*

  That's your proof?

  DELPHI *effortlessly rises into the air.* HARRY/VOLDEMORT
  steps back – amazed.

DELPHI
  I am the Augurey to your Dark Lord, and I am ready to give
  all that I have to serve you.

HARRY/VOLDEMORT *(trying not to show his shock)*
  You learnt flight – from – me?

307

DELPHI
I have tried to follow the path you set.

HARRY/VOLDEMORT
I have never met a witch or a wizard who's attempted to be
my equal before.

DELPHI
Do not mistake me – I would not claim to be worthy of you,
Lord. But I have devoted my life to being a child you could
be proud of.

HARRY/VOLDEMORT *(interrupting)*
I see what you are, and I see what you could be. Daughter.

She looks at him, desperately moved.

DELPHI
Father?

HARRY/VOLDEMORT
Together, the power we could wield.

DELPHI
Father ...

HARRY/VOLDEMORT
Come here, in the light, so I may examine what my blood
made.

DELPHI
Your mission is a mistake. Attacking Harry Potter is a
mistake. He will destroy you.

> HARRY/VOLDEMORT's *hand turns into* HARRY's *hand. He*
> *looks at it astonished and dismayed, and then quickly*
> *pulls it inside his sleeve.*

HARRY/VOLDEMORT
He is a baby.

DELPHI
He has his mother's love, your spell will rebound, destroying
you and making him too powerful and you too weak. You

will recover, to spend the next seventeen years consumed in a battle with him – a battle you will lose.

HARRY/VOLDEMORT's hair begins to sprout, he feels it, he attempts to cover it. He pulls his hood over his head.

HARRY/VOLDEMORT
Then I won't attack him. You are right.

DELPHI
Father?

HARRY/VOLDEMORT shrinks down – he is now more HARRY than VOLDEMORT. He turns his back to DELPHI.

Father?

HARRY (*trying desperately to still sound like VOLDEMORT*)
Your plan is a good one. The fight is off. You have served me well, now come here into the light so I may examine you.

DELPHI sees a door slightly sway open and then be pulled shut. She frowns at it, thinking rapidly, her suspicion growing.

DELPHI
Father . . .

She tries to get a glimpse of his face again, there is almost a dance happening here.

You are not Lord Voldemort.

DELPHI unleashes a bolt from her hand. HARRY matches her.

Incendio!

HARRY
Incendio!

The bolts meet in a beautiful explosion in the middle of the room.

And with her other hand DELPHI *sends bolts to both doors as the others try to open them.*

DELPHI
Potter. Colloportus!

HARRY *looks at the doors, dismayed.*

What? Thought your friends were going to join you did you?

HERMIONE *(from off)*
Harry ... Harry ...

GINNY *(from off)*
She's sealed the doors from your side.

HARRY
Fine. I'll deal with you alone.

He moves to attack her again. But she is far stronger. HARRY's *wand ascends towards her. He is disarmed. He is helpless.*

How did you ... ? What are you?

DELPHI
I've watched you for a long time, Harry Potter. I know you better than my father did.

HARRY
You think you've learnt my weaknesses?

DELPHI
I've studied to be worthy of him! Yes, even though he is the supreme wizard of all time, he will be proud of me. Expulso!

HARRY *rolls away as the floor explodes behind him. He crawls frantically under a church pew, trying to work out how he can fight her.*

Are you crawling away from me? Harry Potter. Hero of the wizarding world. Crawling away like a rat. Wingardium Leviosa!

The church pew ascends into the air.

The question is whether it's worth my time to kill you, knowing that as soon as I stop my father, your destruction will be assured. How to decide? Oh, I'm bored, I'll kill you.

She sends down the pew hard down upon him. It smashes as he rolls desperately away.

ALBUS *emerges from a grate on the floor, neither notice.*

Avada—

ALBUS
Dad . . .

HARRY
Albus! No!

DELPHI
Two of you? Choices, choices. I think I'll kill the boy first. Avada Kedavra!

She fires the Killing Curse at ALBUS *– but* HARRY *throws him out of the way. The bolt smashes into the ground. He fires a bolt back.*

You think you're stronger than me?

HARRY
No. I'm not.

They fire bolts mercilessly at each other as ALBUS *rolls quickly away and slams a spell into one door and then another.*

But we are.

ALBUS *opens both doors with his wand.*

ALBUS
Alohomora! Alohomora!

311

HARRY

I've never fought alone, you see. And I never will.

HERMIONE, RON, GINNY and DRACO emerge from the doors, and fire up their spells at DELPHI, who screams out in exasperation. This is titanic. But she can't fight them all.

There are a series of bangs – and then, overwhelmed, DELPHI tumbles down to the floor.

DELPHI

No . . . No . . .

HERMIONE

Brachiabindo!

She's bound.

HARRY advances towards DELPHI. He doesn't take his eyes off her. All the others stay back.

HARRY

Albus, are you okay?

ALBUS

Yes, Dad, I'm okay.

HARRY still doesn't take his eyes off DELPHI. He's still scared of her.

HARRY

Ginny, has he been injured? I need to know he's safe . . .

GINNY

He insisted. He was the only one small enough to crawl through the grate. I tried to stop him.

HARRY

Just tell me he's okay.

ALBUS

I'm fine, Dad. I promise.

HARRY *keeps advancing towards* DELPHI.

HARRY

A lot of people have tried to hurt me – but my son! You
dare hurt my son!

DELPHI

I only wanted to know my father.

These words take HARRY *by surprise.*

HARRY

You can't remake your life. You'll always be an orphan. That
never leaves you.

DELPHI

Just let me – see him.

HARRY

I can't and I won't.

DELPHI *(truly pitiful)*

Then kill me.

HARRY *thinks a moment.*

HARRY

I can't do that either . . .

ALBUS

What? Dad? She's dangerous.

HARRY

No, Albus . . .

ALBUS

But she's a murderer – I've seen her murder—

HARRY *turns and looks at his son and then at* GINNY.

HARRY

Yes. Albus, she's a murderer, and we're not.

HERMIONE

We have to be better than them.

RON

Yeah, it's annoying but it's what we learnt.

DELPHI

Take my mind. Take my memory. Make me forget who I am.

RON

No. We'll take you back to our time.

HERMIONE

And you'll go to Azkaban. Same as your mother.

DRACO

Where you'll rot.

> HARRY *hears a noise. A hissing noise.*
>
> *And then there is a noise like death – a noise like nothing else we've heard before.*
>
> *Haaarry Potttter . . .*

SCORPIUS

What's that?

HARRY

No. No. Not yet.

ALBUS

What?

RON

Voldemort.

DELPHI

Father?

HERMIONE

Now? Here?

DELPHI

Father!

DRACO

Silencio! (DELPHI *is gagged.*) Wingardium Leviosa! (*She is sent upwards and away.*)

HARRY
He's coming. He's coming right now.

> VOLDEMORT *comes through the back of stage, and across it, and walks down into the auditorium. He brings death with him. And everyone knows it.*

ACT FOUR SCENE TWELVE

GODRIC'S HOLLOW, 1981

HARRY *looks after* VOLDEMORT *helplessly.*

HARRY
Voldemort is going to kill my mum and dad, and there's nothing I can do to stop him.

DRACO
That's not true.

SCORPIUS
Dad, now is not the time . . .

ALBUS
There is something you could do – to stop him. But you won't.

DRACO
That's heroic.

GINNY *takes* HARRY's *hand.*

GINNY
You don't have to watch, Harry. We can go home.

HARRY
I'm letting it happen . . . of course I have to watch.

HERMIONE
Then we'll all witness it.

RON
> We'll all watch.

> *We hear unfamiliar voices . . .*

JAMES *(from off)*
> Lily, take Harry and go! It's him! Go! Run! I'll hold him
> off . . .

> *There is a blast, and then a laugh.*

> You keep away, you understand – you keep away.

VOLDEMORT *(from off)*
> Avada Kedavra!

>> HARRY *flinches as green light flashes around the*
>> *auditorium.*

>> ALBUS *takes his hand.* HARRY *grasps hold of it. He needs*
>> *it.*

ALBUS
> He did everything he could.

>> GINNY *rises beside* HARRY, *and takes his other hand. He*
>> *leans into them, they're holding him up now.*

HARRY
> That's my mum, at the window. I can see my mother, she
> looks beautiful.

> *There's the sound of banging as doors are blasted off.*

LILY *(from off)*
> Not Harry, not Harry, please not Harry . . .

VOLDEMORT *(from off)*
> Stand aside, you silly girl . . . stand aside now . . .

LILY *(from off)*
> Not Harry, please no, take me, kill me instead . . .

VOLDEMORT *(from off)*
This is my last warning—

LILY *(from off)*
Not Harry! Please ... have mercy ... have mercy ... not my son! Please – I'll do anything.

VOLDEMORT *(from off)*
Avada Kedavra!

> *And it's like lightning passes through* HARRY's *body. He's sent to the floor, a pure mess of grief.*
>
> *And a noise like a shrunken scream descends and ascends around us.*
>
> *And we just watch.*
>
> *And slowly what was there is no longer there.*
>
> *And the stage transforms and rotates.*
>
> *And* HARRY *and his family and his friends are rotated off and away.*

ACT FOUR   SCENE THIRTEEN

GODRIC'S HOLLOW, INSIDE JAMES AND
LILY POTTER'S HOUSE, 1981

And we're in the ruins of a house. A house that has undergone a vicious attack.

HAGRID walks through the ruins.

HAGRID
James?

> *He looks about himself.*

Lily??

> *He walks slowly, unwilling to see too much too soon. He is entirely overwhelmed.*
> *And then he sees them, and he stops, and he says nothing.*

Oh. Oh. That's not – that's not – I weren't . . . they told me, but – I were hoping for better . . .

> *He looks at them and bows his head. He mutters a few words and then takes some crumpled flowers from his deep pockets and lays them on the floor.*

I'm sorry, they told me, he told me, Dumbledore told me, I can't wait with yeh. Them Muggles are coming yeh see with their flashing blues and they won't 'preciate a big lummox like me would they?

He lets out a sob.

Hard though it is to leave yeh. I want yeh to know – yeh won't be forgotten – not by me – not by anyfolk.

And then he hears a sound – the sound of a baby snuffling. HAGRID *turns towards it, walking with more intensity now.*
He looks down and stands over the crib, which seems to radiate light.

Well. Hello. Yeh must be Harry. Hello, Harry Potter. I'm Rubeus Hagrid. And I'm gonna be yer friend whether yeh like it or not. 'Cos yeh've had it tough, not that yeh know it yet. An' yer gonna need friends. Now yeh best come with me don't yeh think?

As flashing blue lights fill the room giving it an almost ethereal glow, he lifts HARRY *gently into his arms.*
And then – without looking back – he strides away through the house.
And we descend into soft black.

ACT FOUR SCENE FOURTEEN

HOGWARTS, CLASSROOM

SCORPIUS and ALBUS run into a room, full of excitement. They slam the door after themselves.

SCORPIUS

    I can't quite believe I did that.

ALBUS

    I can't quite believe you did that either.

SCORPIUS

    Rose Granger-Weasley. I asked out Rose Granger-Weasley.

ALBUS

    And she said no.

SCORPIUS

    But I asked her. I planted the acorn. The acorn that will grow into our eventual marriage.

ALBUS

    You are aware that you're an utter fantasist.

SCORPIUS

    And I'd agree with you – only Polly Chapman did ask me to the School Ball . . .

ALBUS

    In an alternate reality where you were significantly – really

significantly, more popular – a different girl asked you out –
and that means—

SCORPIUS

And yes, logic would dictate I should be pursuing Polly – or
allowing her to pursue me – she's a notorious beauty after
all – but a Rose is a Rose.

ALBUS

You know logic would dictate that you're a freak? Rose hates
you.

SCORPIUS

Correction, she used to hate me, but did you see the look in
her eyes when I asked? That wasn't hate, that was pity.

ALBUS

And pity's good?

SCORPIUS

Pity is a start my friend, a foundation on which to build a
palace – a palace of love.

ALBUS

I honestly thought I'd be the first of us to get a girlfriend.

SCORPIUS

Oh, you will, undoubtedly, probably that new smoky-eyed
Potions professor – she's old enough for you, right?

ALBUS

I don't have a thing about older women!

SCORPIUS

And you've got time – a lot of time – to seduce her. Because
Rose is going to take years to persuade.

ALBUS

I admire your confidence.

> ROSE *comes past them on the stairs, she looks at them*
> *both.*

ROSE
Hi.

Neither boy knows quite how to reply – she looks at
SCORPIUS.

ROSE
This is only going to be weird if you let it be weird.

SCORPIUS
Received and entirely understood.

ROSE
Okay. 'Scorpion King'.

She walks off with a smile on her face. SCORPIUS *and*
ALBUS *look at each other.* ALBUS *grins and punches*
SCORPIUS *on the arm.*

ALBUS
Maybe you're right – pity is a start.

SCORPIUS
Are you heading to Quidditch? Slytherin are playing
Hufflepuff – it's a big one—

ALBUS
I thought we hated Quidditch?

SCORPIUS
People can change. Besides, I've been practising. I think I
might make the team eventually. Come on.

ALBUS
I can't. My dad's arranged to come up—

SCORPIUS
He's taking time away from the Ministry?

ALBUS
He wants to go on a walk – something to show me – share
with me – something.

SCORPIUS
A walk?

ALBUS

I know, I think it's a bonding thing or something similarly vomit-inducing. Still, you know, I think I'll go.

SCORPIUS *reaches in and hugs* ALBUS.

What's this? I thought we decided we don't hug.

SCORPIUS

I wasn't sure. Whether we should. In this new version of us I had in my head.

ALBUS

Better ask Rose if it's the right thing to do.

SCORPIUS

Ha! Yeah. Right.

The two boys dislocate and grin at each other.

ALBUS

I'll see you at dinner.

ACT FOUR   SCENE FIFTEEN

A BEAUTIFUL HILL

HARRY *and* ALBUS *walk up a hill on a beautiful summer's day.*
They say nothing, enjoying the sun on their faces as they climb.

HARRY
So are you ready?

ALBUS
For what?

HARRY
Well, there's the fourth-year exams – and then the fifth
year – big year – in my fifth year I did—

He looks at ALBUS. *He smiles. He talks quickly.*

I did a lot of stuff. Some of it good. Some of it bad. A lot of
it quite confusing.

ALBUS
Good to know.

HARRY *smiles.*

I got to watch them – you know – for a bit – your mum and
dad. They were – you had fun together. Your dad used to
love to do this smoke ring thing with you where you . . .
well, you couldn't stop giggling.

HARRY

    Yes?

ALBUS

    I think you'd have liked them. And I think me, Lily and
James would have liked them too.

    HARRY nods. There's a slightly uncomfortable silence.
    Both are trying to reach each other here, both are failing.

HARRY

    You know, I thought I'd lost him – Voldemort – I thought
I'd lost him – and then my scar started hurting again and
I had dreams of him and I could even speak Parseltongue
again and I started to feel like I'd not changed at all – that
he'd never let me go –

ALBUS

    And had he?

HARRY

    The part of me that was Voldemort died a long time ago,
but it wasn't enough to be physically rid of him – I had to
be mentally rid of him. And that – is a lot to learn for a
forty-year-old man.

    He looks at ALBUS.

    That thing I said to you – it was unforgiveable, and I can't
ask you to forget it but I can hope we move past it.

    I'm going to try to be a better dad for you, Albus. I am going
to try and – be honest with you and . . .

ALBUS

    Dad, you don't need to—

HARRY

    You told me you don't think I'm scared of anything, and
that – I mean, I'm scared of everything. I mean, I'm afraid
of the dark, did you know that?

ALBUS

Harry Potter is afraid of the dark?

HARRY

I don't like small spaces and – I've never told anyone this but I don't much like – *(he hesitates before saying this)* pigeons.

ALBUS

You don't like pigeons?

HARRY *(he scrunches up his face)*

Nasty, pecky, dirty things. They give me the creeps.

ALBUS

But pigeons are harmless!

HARRY

I know. But the thing that scares me most, Albus Severus Potter, is being a dad to you. Because I'm operating without wires here. Most people at least have a dad to base themselves on – and either try to be or try not to be. I've got nothing – or very little. So I'm learning, okay? And I'm going to try with everything I've got – to be a good dad for you.

ALBUS

And I'll try and be a better son. I know I'm not James, Dad, I'll never be like you two—

HARRY

James is nothing like me.

ALBUS

Isn't he?

HARRY

Everything comes easy for James. My childhood was a constant struggle.

ALBUS

So was mine. So you're saying – am I – like you?

HARRY *smiles at* ALBUS.

HARRY

Actually you're more like your mum – bold, fierce, funny –
which I like – which I think makes you a pretty great son.

ALBUS

I almost destroyed the world.

HARRY

Delphi wasn't going anywhere, Albus – you brought her out
into the light and you found a way for us to fight her. You
may not see it now, but you saved us.

ALBUS

But shouldn't I have done better?

HARRY

You don't think I ask myself the same questions?

ALBUS (*stomach sinking further, he knows this is not what his dad
would do*)

And then – when we caught her – I wanted to kill her.

HARRY

You'd watched her murder Craig, you were angry Albus, and
that's okay. And you wouldn't have done it.

ALBUS

How do you know that? Maybe that's my Slytherin side.
Maybe that's what the Sorting Hat saw in me.

HARRY

I don't understand your head, Albus – actually, you know
what, you're a teenager, I shouldn't be able to understand
your head, but I do understand your heart. I didn't – for a
long time – but thanks to this – 'escapade' – I know what
you got in there. Slytherin, Gryffindor, whatever label
you've been given – I know – know – that heart is a good
one – yeah, whether you like it or not, you're on your way to
being some wizard.

ALBUS

Oh, I'm not going to be a wizard, I'm going into pigeon
racing. I'm quite excited about it.

HARRY *grins.*

HARRY

Those names you have – they shouldn't be a burden. Albus
Dumbledore had his trials too you know – and Severus
Snape, well, you know all about him—

ALBUS

They were good men.

HARRY

They were great men, with huge flaws, and you know
what – those flaws almost made them greater.

ALBUS *looks around himself.*

ALBUS

Dad? Why are we here?

HARRY

This is where I often come.

ALBUS

But this is a graveyard . . .

HARRY

And here is Cedric's grave . . .

ALBUS

Dad?

HARRY

The boy who was killed – Craig Bowker – how well did you
know him?

ALBUS

Not well enough.

HARRY

I didn't know Cedric well enough either. He could have played Quidditch for England. Or been a brilliant Auror. He could have been anything. And Amos is right – he was stolen. So I come here. Just to say sorry. When I can.

ALBUS

That's a – good thing to do.

ALBUS *joins his dad in front of* CEDRIC's *grave.* HARRY *smiles at his son and looks up at the sky.*

HARRY

I think it's going to be a nice day.

He touches his son's shoulder. And the two of them – just slightly – melt together.

ALBUS *(smiles)*
So do I.

THE END

Harry Potter and the Cursed Child Parts One and Two was first produced by Sonia Friedman Productions, Colin Callender and Harry Potter Theatrical Productions. It premiered at the Palace Theatre, London, on 30 July 2016 with the following cast.

Cast names in alphabetical order

CRAIG BOWKER JR	Jeremy Ang Jones
MOANING MYRTLE, LILY POTTER SR	Annabel Baldwin
UNCLE VERNON, SEVERUS SNAPE, LORD VOLDEMORT	Paul Bentall
SCORPIUS MALFOY	Anthony Boyle
ALBUS POTTER	Sam Clemmett
HERMIONE GRANGER	Noma Dumezweni
POLLY CHAPMAN	Claudia Grant
HAGRID, SORTING HAT	Chris Jarman
YANN FREDERICKS	James Le Lacheur
AUNT PETUNIA, MADAM HOOCH, DOLORES UMBRIDGE	Helena Lymbery
AMOS DIGGORY, ALBUS DUMBLEDORE	Barry McCarthy
TROLLEY WITCH, PROFESSOR McGONAGALL	Sandy McDade
STATION MASTER	Adam McNamara
GINNY POTTER	Poppy Miller
CEDRIC DIGGORY, JAMES POTTER JR, JAMES POTTER SR	Tom Milligan

DUDLEY DURSLEY, KARL JENKINS, VIKTOR KRUM	Jack North
HARRY POTTER	Jamie Parker
DRACO MALFOY	Alex Price
BANE	Nuno Silva
ROSE GRANGER-WEASLEY, YOUNG HERMIONE	Cherrelle Skeete
DELPHI DIGGORY	Esther Smith
RON WEASLEY	Paul Thornley
YOUNG HARRY POTTER	Rudi Goodman Alfred Jones Bili Keogh Ewan Rutherford Nathaniel Smith Dylan Standen
LILY POTTER JR	Zoe Brough Cristina Fray Christiana Hutchings

OTHER ROLES PLAYED BY

Nicola Alexis, Jeremy Ang Jones, Rosemary Annabella,
Annabel Baldwin, Jack Bennett, Paul Bentall, Morag Cross,
Claudia Grant, James Howard, Lowri James, Chris Jarman,
Martin Johnston, James Le Lacheur, Helena Lymbery,
Barry McCarthy, Andrew McDonald, Adam McNamara,
Tom Milligan, Jack North, Stuart Ramsay, Nuno Silva,
Cherrelle Skeete

SWINGS

Helen Aluko, Morag Cross, Chipo Kureya, Tom Mackley,
Joshua Wyatt

Nuno Silva	Movement Captain
Jack North	Assistant Movement Captain
Morag Cross	Voice Captain

CREATIVE AND PRODUCTION TEAM

Original Story	J.K. Rowling, John Tiffany, Jack Thorne
Playwright	Jack Thorne
Director	John Tiffany
Movement Director	Steven Hoggett
Set Designer	Christine Jones
Costume Designer	Katrina Lindsay
Composer & Arranger	Imogen Heap
Lighting Designer	Neil Austin
Sound Designer	Gareth Fry
Illusions & Magic	Jamie Harrison
Music Supervisor & Arranger	Martin Lowe
Casting Director	Julia Horan CDG
Production Manager	Gary Beestone
Production Stage Manager	Sam Hunter
Associate Director	Des Kennedy
Associate Movement Director	Neil Bettles
Associate Set Designer	Brett J. Banakis
Associate Sound Designer	Pete Malkin

Illusions & Magic Associate	Chris Fisher
Casting Associate	Lotte Hines
Assistant Lighting Designer	Adam King
Costume Design Supervisor	Sabine Lemaître
Hair, Wigs & Make-up	Carole Hancock
Props Supervisors	Lisa Buckley, Mary Halliday
Music Editor	Phij Adams
Music Production	Imogen Heap
Special Effects	Jeremy Chernick
Video Design	Finn Ross, Ash Woodward
Dialect Coach	Daniele Lydon
Voice Coach	Richard Ryder
Company Stage Manager	Richard Clayton
Stage Manager	Jordan Noble-Davies
Deputy Stage Manager	Jenefer Tait
Assistant Stage Managers	Oliver Bagwell Purefoy, Tom Gilding, Sally Inch, Ben Sherratt
Resident Director	Pip Minnithorpe
Head of Wardrobe	Amy Gillot
Deputy Head of Wardrobe	Laura Watkins
Wardrobe Assistants	Kate Anderson, Leanne Hired
Dressers	George Amielle, Melissa Cooke, Rosie Etheridge, John Ovenden, Emilee Swift
Head of Hair, Wigs & Make-up	Nina Van Houten
Deputy Head of Hair, Wigs & Make-up	Alice Townes
Hair, Wigs & Make-up Assistants	Charlotte Briscoe, Jacob Fessey, Cassie Murphie
Head of Sound	Chris Reid

Deputy Head of Sound	Rowena Edwards
Sound No. 3	Laura Caplin
SFX Operator	Callum Donaldson
Head of Automation	Josh Peters
Deputy Head of Automation	Jamie Lawrence
Automation No. 3	Jamie Robson
Show Chief LX	David Treanor
Performer Flying Technician	Paul Gurney
Chaperones	David Russell, Eleanor Dowling
General Management	Sonia Friedman Productions
Executive Director	Diane Benjamin
Executive Producer	Pam Skinner
Associate Producer	Fiona Stewart
Assistant Producer	Ben Canning
General Management Assistant	Max Bittleston
Production Assistant	Imogen Clare-Wood
Marketing Manager	Laura Jane Elliott
Revenue Manager	Mark Payn
Associate Producer (Development)	Lucie Lovatt
Development Assistant	Lydia Rynne
Literary Associate	Jack Bradley
Office Assistant	Jordan Eaton
House Seats Assistant	Vicky Ngoma

BIOGRAPHIES OF THE ORIGINAL STORY TEAM

J.K. ROWLING
Original story

J.K. Rowling is the author of the seven Harry Potter novels, which have sold over 450 million copies and have been translated into 79 languages, and three companion books originally published for charity. She is also the author of *The Casual Vacancy*, a novel for adults published in 2012, and, under the pseudonym of Robert Galbraith, is the author of the Cormoran Strike crime series. J.K. Rowling is making her screenwriting debut and is a producer on the film *Fantastic Beasts and Where to Find Them*, a further extension of the Wizarding World, due for release in November 2016.

JOHN TIFFANY
Original story and director

John Tiffany directed *Once*, for which he was the recipient of multiple awards both in the West End and on Broadway. As Associate Director of the Royal Court, his work includes *The Twits*, *Hope* and *The Pass*. He was the director of *Let the Right One In* for the National Theatre of Scotland, which transferred to the Royal Court, West End and St Ann's Warehouse. His other work for the National Theatre of Scotland includes *Macbeth* (also Broadway), *Enquirer*, *The Missing*, *Peter Pan*, *The House of Bernarda Alba*, *Transform Caithness: Hunter*, *Be Near Me*, *Nobody Will Ever Forgive Us*, *The Bacchae*, *Black Watch*, for which he won the Olivier and Critics' Circle Best Director Awards, *Elizabeth Gordon Quinn* and *Home: Glasgow*. Other recent credits include *The Glass Menagerie* at ART and on Broadway and *The Ambassador* at BAM. Tiffany was Associate Director of the National Theatre of Scotland from 2005 to 2012, and was a Radcliffe Fellow at Harvard University in the 2010–2011 academic year.

JACK THORNE
Original story and playwright

Jack Thorne writes for theatre, film, television and radio. His theatre credits include *Hope* and *Let the Right One In*, both directed by John Tiffany, *The Solid Life of Sugar Water* for the Graeae Theatre Company and the National Theatre, *Bunny* for the Edinburgh Fringe Festival, *Stacy* for the Trafalgar Studios, and *2nd May 1997* and *When You Cure Me* for the Bush. His adaptations include *The Physicists* for the Donmar Warehouse and *Stuart: A Life Backwards* for HighTide. On film his credits include *War Book*, *A Long Way Down* and *The Scouting Book for Boys*. For television his credits include *The Last Panthers*, *Don't Take My Baby*, *This Is England*, *The Fades*, *Glue*, *Cast-Offs* and *National Treasure*. He won BAFTAs in 2016 for Best Mini-Series (*This Is England '90*) and Best Single Drama (*Don't Take My Baby*), and in 2012 for Best Drama Series (*The Fades*) and Best Mini-Series (*This Is England '88*).

ACKNOWLEDGEMENTS

All the actors from the Cursed Child workshops, Mel Kenyon, Rachel Taylor, Alexandria Horton, Imogen Clare-Wood, Florence Rees, Jenefer Tait, David Nock, Rachel Mason, Colin, Neil, Sonia, everyone at SFP and The Blair Partnership, Rebecca Salt from JKR PR, Nica Burns and all the staff at the Palace Theatre, and, of course, our incredible cast who helped shape every word.